Alexander Technique

in Everyday Activity

Improve how you sit, stand, walk, work and run

Seán Carey

First published in 2015 by HITE

HITE Limited, 10 Harley Street, London W1G 9PF

Email: info@hiteltd.co.uk
Website: www.hiteltd.co.uk

10 9 8 7 6 5 4 3 2 1

A CIP catalogue for this book is available from
the British Library.

ISBN 978 0 95689 975 0

Cover picture of 'Loretta Manson walking in
Shoreditch' by Ryan Carey

Editor Dr Dalton Exley

Book and cover design: Roger Greenhough
rog@monkeyboydesign.co.uk

Printed and bound in India by Imprint Digital

Contents

Foreword

How many of us think about how we move? Walking, sitting, lying, moving generally are things we do unconsciously all the time, unless we have pain or discomfort. Yet the way we perform these habitual actions can be very powerful cultural and tribal indicators.

Many of you will have seen World War Two escape movies, where the plucky British escapee is caught by the Germans on the railway station. How, despite the elaborate disguise, do they know this isn't just another German businessman on his way to work? They may well have had prior information of course, but one of the dead giveaways is the way our escapee walks. He walks, unconsciously, like fellow Englishmen of his class and culture, not like Germans in that part of the country.

Similarly, how often have you searched for a friend in a crowd, only to recognise them at a considerable distance by their walk?

Something so apparently trivial can speak volumes.

We all have our own way of moving which may, or more probably may not, be the best for us. What I love about the Alexander Technique is that the repositioning you learn, which at first may feel very strange, can lead after a while to a noticeable absence of bodily aches and pains.

In addition there is the often unexpected emotional connection: an aligned/relaxed body which has a direct effect on your feeling of well-being. I vividly remember that experience of rushing from work to an Alexander lesson with Seán Carey, tired and stressed, and leaving an hour later, feeling not only six inches taller and several pounds lighter, but rested and clearer in my mind – as though that heavy lead weight had been lifted from both mind and body. The Alexander Technique is the perfect antidote to the busy lives we lead, and this absorbing book takes the reader gently through the techniques to achieve that equilibrium.

Rosalynde Lowe CBE

Former Chair of the Queen's Nursing Institute; Member of the Joint Board of Brighton and Sussex Medical School

Acknowledgements

The idea for this book came about after I wrote *Alexander Technique: the Ground Rules*, based on interviews with FM Alexander's niece and first-generation Alexander teacher Marjory Barlow. After finishing that text in 2011, the fourth book I had co-authored, I thought the time was right to record some of the other things I had discovered about the technique having worked with so many inspirational teachers before, during and after I qualified as a teacher.

Encouraged by my friend and publisher Kamal Thapen the text began to take shape as I set about describing and analysing activities, such as standing, walking, sitting, bending and running that all able-bodied humans on the planet perform. I was further encouraged by my Alexander Technique teacher friend and colleague Dr Barry Collins. Barry also very kindly read sections of text as I produced them – thanks to the internet even when he was on holiday in far-flung parts – and provided critical feedback and support which has been immensely helpful. I owe him a huge debt of gratitude.

I would like to thank my students who have read sections of the book and others who have made a contribution. They are Martin Davies, Rowena Eardley, Matthew Gardner, Chris Knowles, Simon Fitzgerald, Jonathan Freeman, Zandra Israel, Adrian and Nicola Lenthall, Katherine Lorigan, Karen Morrish, Laura North, Lyn Parkyns, Sue Roden, Dr Salem Saumtally, and Patricia and Peter Stroud.

I am particularly indebted to two of my long-time students, Miranda Bayliss and Linda Jowsey, who read various versions of the manuscript, offering comments and criticisms, which helped enormously. Music therapist and Alexander Technique teacher Dr Gary Ansdell also read the manuscript and offered me the benefit of his considerable knowledge and wisdom. I am extremely grateful for his contribution.

I would like to pay tribute to those first generation teachers taught by FM Alexander with whom I had lessons. Alas, they have all passed away. Nevertheless their teaching legacy continues to provide inspiration and good practice for me and for many of my fellow teachers. They are Marjory Barlow, Walter Carrington, Sidney Holland, Elisabeth Walker and Peggy Williams.

I would also like to thank other teachers who have made a significant contribution to my understanding of the Alexander Technique. They include directors of my training course, Elisabeth Atkinson, Don Burton and Adam Nott, and visiting teachers Diana Aubrey, Jean Clark, Ray Evans, Lindy Field, Everard Peters, Ilan Reichel, Ken Thompson, Elisabeth Waterhouse and Christina Wilton.

There are many other teachers from whom I have learned a lot. Special thanks go to Paul Collins for his innovative insights into running. I also thank Anne Battye, Dilys Carrington, Margaret Edis, Brita Forrstrom, Loretta Manson and Claire Rennie for their inspiration.

I must pay a special tribute to John Nicholls who has given much thought into how the insights produced by Alexander and the first generation of teachers, can be translated into more easily understood concepts and practices for students.

I'm very grateful to my editor Dr Dalton Exley for his patience, help and advice in shaping the manuscript and designing the book. What was originally a much larger text has become smaller, and all the better for that.

Thanks also to Holly Blake, Nathan Campbell, Staffan Scherz and Mark Wordingham, who gave permission for their photographs to be used. I also thank Ryan Carey for taking many of the photographs used throughout the text and Sally Barton for the illustrations. In addition, my sincere gratitude goes to our models Rory Heath and Loretta Manson.

Finally, I thank all the many students I have had the privilege to teach, and from whom I have learnt a lot. Any errors or shortcomings in the book are entirely my responsibility.

Seán Carey

London

For Nalini and Ryan

Preface

It's a warm, sunny summer's day. I am taking my daily after-lunch walk near my home when I see coming towards me a slim, smartly-dressed white-haired man carrying two shopping bags, one in each hand. They do not look that heavy. But he does. The man is, I would guess, in his mid-60s – not old by the standards of contemporary Western society – yet there is no spring in his step. Instead, he is plodding along. I also observe that he is markedly stooped and looking at the ground a few feet in front of him, seemingly in a world of his own. I think to myself that he would have been several inches taller when he was younger. As we get closer and he hears my footsteps, he looks up and pulls himself up into what he obviously thinks is a better posture. The stoop remains, however. We have never met before but nevertheless we exchange greetings as is customary in this part of the world. 'Hello,' he says. 'Hello,' I reply. 'It's a beautiful day,' he says. 'It is, let's hope it lasts,' I respond mindful of the often sudden changes in weather in the south-east of England.

Immediately I find myself wondering how the man has ended up in that shape. Is it hereditary? Is it congenital? Does he have an on-going medical condition such as osteoporosis? Has he become that shape because of the way he has used himself throughout his life? Or has it come about from a combination of some of these factors? I reflect that it is entirely possible that he has ended up the way he has through a sudden or, more likely, gradual deterioration in his general coordination.

If so there could be a variety of reasons. Had he had spent a lifetime slouching at a desk, writing with a pen in the earlier part of his life and using a keyboard in later years? Could he as a teenager have been tall relative to his contemporaries and had adopted a stoop to fit into the peer group, which then affected the development of the spine? Or a keen cyclist who had assumed a C-shaped position on his bike because the handlebars were too far forward? Alternatively perhaps he had been a surgeon, or a dentist, who spent too many years crouching over his patients. The number of possible explanations is huge. In any event, he is the way he is. Of course if he has ended up in the shape he is in because of the way he has used his body, it is a great pity. Things could have been otherwise for this man, as indeed it could be for so many of us, if we just learned some basic lessons in kinaesthetic education.

My background and some history

We all have our own stories. My involvement with the Alexander Technique followed after a serious motorcycle accident.

One summer I was working on a building site at Heathrow Airport. My aim was to make sufficient money to tide me over the rest of the university year. I had an easy job. It involved occasionally holding a pole so that a surveyor, who was using a theodolite, could make precise map measurements to ensure that buildings ended up where they were supposed to.

One day the surveyor I was working with gave me a copy of Dr Wilfred Barlow's *The Alexander Principle*, and suggested I read it, as he had found it fascinating. I had never heard of the Alexander Technique, but I read the book very quickly, before returning it. I was intrigued by the concept that the way we use our bodies from moment to moment affects functioning (including, in part, our capacity to think and feel) and has profound consequences for health and well-being. I was even more intrigued that we could learn to modify our general coordination in movement and stillness. This was a very attractive idea because a couple of years earlier my lower right leg and foot had been badly broken after a car ran into the back of the motorcycle on which I was riding pillion, and I was still dealing with the aftermath.

A few years later, when I could afford it, I went for my first lesson in the Alexander Technique. I did not know what to expect, but after a brief discussion about why I had come, my teacher moved me in and out of the chair two or three times and then laid me down on a wooden table covered with a blanket.

I became aware that my neck and head, which was supported by a small pile of paperback books, were a primary focus of attention for my teacher. She would constantly return to stand behind me and then place her hands around the muscles of my neck, producing what felt like a gentle stretch so that my head released away from my trunk. My teacher would then occasionally slowly rotate my head a little, while telling me to continue to allow its weight to be supported by the books and her hands. I was also instructed to allow my legs and arms to be moved without my helping in any way. I found these ostensibly simple things incredibly hard to do. By anticipating or controlling the movement I was causing interference. I was assured by my teacher that this was a common experience among new students.

That first lesson in the Alexander Technique was very relaxing though, even if what was involved was more than a little mysterious. However I was open-minded enough to accept something new. Indeed afterwards I can distinctly remember walking along the road feeling considerably lighter than when I went in. I also had a sensation that my shoulders were operating differently, as if a coat hanger had been placed inside my upper torso. It struck me then that the Alexander Technique was certainly quite different from the physiotherapy treatment I had experienced after the full-leg plaster (which I had endured for six months) had been cut away by my orthopaedic surgeon, revealing a badly wasted leg. Wherein lay the difference? In my experience of physiotherapy there was little or no emphasis on *how* I was walking – once I had discarded crutches and walking sticks the aim of my physiotherapists was to get me moving upright in one way or another so that I could be discharged. By contrast in the Alexander Technique great emphasis was placed on getting an improved working of the head, neck and back relationship in conjunction with an efficient working of the legs and arms so that walking could occur more efficiently.

On the advice of my Alexander teacher I had three lessons a week for four weeks, two lessons for four weeks and then one a week thereafter. I was impressed with what I was discovering and learning. I was practising Alexander lying down on a daily basis and also intermittently thinking about how I got in and out of a chair, and my method of walking. Overall I found that I was moving more easily. Since early childhood I had been interested in sport and movement – I enjoyed athletics, playing football, rugby and cricket, and practised karate at secondary school and at university – so the Alexander Technique fitted well with those enthusiasms. So much so that later I joined a three-year Alexander Technique teacher training course, qualifying in 1986.

Throughout this period of my life the number of books on the technique was relatively small – four texts written by FM Alexander and a few others. A great deal of knowledge of the Alexander Technique is embedded in oral-kinaesthetic traditions. Much of this information is transmitted on training courses and workshops. Only a fraction has been written down. Because of my background in the social sciences I was acutely aware that unless it was recorded it would be lost. That concern prompted me in the early and mid-1990s to carry out a series of interviews with two teachers, Marjory Barlow and Walter Carrington, who had been trained by Alexander in the 1930s and to turn those conversations into books, so that at least some aspects of the history and practice of the technique would be available for current and future generations.

When Frederick Matthias Alexander, the founder of the Alexander Technique, died in 1955 there was no nominated successor. The result was that a number of London-based teachers – Marjory and Wilfred Barlow, Walter Carrington, Patrick Macdonald, and Peter Scott – took it upon themselves to continue or organise independent teacher training courses, so that the technique would survive. At the suggestion of Dr Barlow, those different Alexander 'tribes' cooperated to form the Society of Teachers of the Alexander Technique (STAT) in 1958.

I am a beneficiary of this legacy. I trained at the Alexander Teaching Associates (ATA), a STAT-approved course in east London, and was fortunate to be exposed to the three dominant teaching traditions in the UK – those pioneered by Carrington, Macdonald and the Barlows. ATA students also had input from a number of visiting Alexander teachers from the US and Europe. After I qualified I worked on four STAT-approved Alexander Technique training courses in London. Throughout this time I had lessons from a number of teachers taught by Alexander. This, among other things, allowed me to ponder differences in teaching styles and the interface between tradition and innovation in the technique. All these experiences have informed a major part of the content of this book.

Using this book to your advantage

In recent years a huge number of introductory books on the Alexander Technique have been published, but very few add much to what's already been produced and only a handful are aimed at students wishing to explore with their teachers, and by themselves, deeper aspects of the Alexander Technique. So in this book I have attempted to go well beyond the subject matter of simple introductory texts.

Anyone can read this book and gain from it, but you will get a lot more out of it if you have had some experience of the Alexander Technique and want to know more about the process of what the American philosopher John Dewey called 'thinking in activity'. After the two introductory chapters, on Alexander's discovery and on inhibition and direction, those that follow analyse a sequence of basic human movements of the sort that all able-bodied people in any society perform. I start with standing, before examining walking, sitting, bending, using the arms and hands, lying down and running. The book concludes with a section on frequently asked questions to which I have tried to provide answers.

In order to avoid complexity and labouring the obvious, when describing specific activities such as standing, sitting, bending, walking and running for the most part I have simplified terms so that 'I' stands for a teacher of the Alexander Technique and 'you' denotes a student. Sometimes I have described activities as if I am present using my hands and verbal instructions to guide you and sometimes I have written them up as if you were on your own thinking through and applying what you have learnt in lessons.

Different Alexander activities are described in detail. Do not worry if you do not understand everything on first reading. You can always come back later after you have had more Alexander lessons, when I'm sure things will be clearer. So that you have a handy reference I have summarised some of them using boxed text. Alexander activities that are relevant but not central to my theme have also been placed in boxed text. Of course you do not have to read the chapters in sequence. Instead you can find a topic that you are interested in, say, sitting on a chair, playing the piano or dancing, Alexander lying down, walking or running, and go through the relevant sections, as they can be read as stand-alone passages.

I also hope that this book encourages you to experiment with inhibition, direction and movement in the diverse activities that make up your life but which are not covered here.

In doing so do not be afraid of making mistakes. Finding out about your biomechanically inefficient habits is an important component of learning the Alexander Technique. Like so much else in life denial does not take us very far. It's far better to embrace your errors, work out a better way to proceed, and then try again. Over time you will surely improve.

This book is not an encyclopaedic account of the Alexander Technique – rather, the activities described are those which I have found particularly helpful and which, depending on their ability and interests, I teach my students. Other Alexander teachers will no doubt have different perspectives on activities that they regard as central to the method. Does that mean, as some claim, that anything done in the name of the Alexander Technique is the Alexander Technique? The answer is: definitely not. Why? Simply because Alexander's brilliant and deeply counterintuitive concepts and practices, including the importance of conscious inhibition and direction, the faulty manner in which the kinaesthetic system typically works, the attention to means rather than ends and crucially, the effects of good and bad coordination on breathing, vocalisation and other movements, are unique and have stood the test of time.

I have attempted to place the Alexander Technique in a contemporary context by drawing on relevant interdisciplinary research. At all times, though, I have tried to write in a non-technical way using the minimum amount of anatomical and other specialised terms. Some topics have been placed in boxed text which you can skip if you are not interested, although if you are, references can be found at the end of the book.

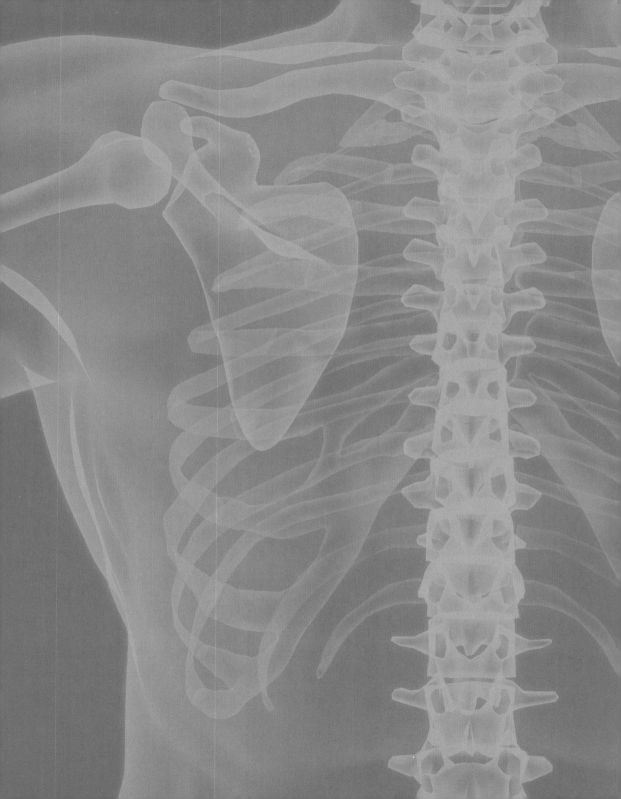

Chapter **1** – *Introduction*

'The body is man's first and most natural instrument'

Marcel Mauss

'Breathing, standing, walking, sitting, although innate, along with our growth, are apt, as movements, to suffer from defects in our ways of doing them'

Sir Charles Sherrington

Movement patterns

In this book I aim to show you how the Alexander Technique is relevant to your everyday practices, such as sitting, standing, carrying shopping bags, retrieving an item dropped on the floor, gesticulation, speaking, opening a door, using a toothbrush, as well as walking and running. These activities are familiar to everyone in our society. Moreover they are all repeated activities that have very significant consequences for our bodies if we do them 'badly'.

If we are to better understand our diverse movement patterns it is necessary to take into account learning through individual trial and error, including coping strategies, which are often a response to injury, trauma, stress, and congenital and genetic conditions. But whatever the origins, it is essential to acknowledge that our habitual patterns of movement are deeply embedded at a number of interconnected levels – social, cultural, political, economic, psychological and neurophysiological.

The power of society and culture

Although the Alexander Technique has been enormously influential in mainstream forms of Western music and drama, I only occasionally refer to these specialist activities. Instead I draw on my experience of teaching the Alexander Technique to people from a wide variety of backgrounds, as well as my training in social anthropology, an academic discipline which, amongst other things, uses observation to document and analyse the power of society and culture to create and shape our routine, everyday behaviour.

An anthropological perspective reveals that whatever our innate or biological needs we are social animals with an enormous capacity for learning. Much of what we take for granted about our life world is not 'natural' but a matter of shared cultural convention. Unlike other species, including those most closely related to us such as bonobos and chimpanzees, humans are capable of an astonishing variety of behaviours. This explains why different modes of conduct are found in different societies today and in the past. Social and cultural processes inform and shape how we speak; what we eat; the clothes we wear; the music we listen to; the manner in which we express emotions; and of course the ways in which we use our bodies when doing these and a myriad other things. 'All the world's a stage,' says Jaques in Shakespeare's *As You Like It*, 'and all the men and women merely players.' It's a brilliant metaphor. In our complex, diverse 'open' society life is often very much like a performance. And that observation reveals something else of great importance about our everyday experience. The roles we are allocated or, more occasionally, choose – for example, as son or daughter, doctor or patient, teacher or student, diner or waiter, cricket player or umpire and so on – orient and constrain our behaviour in important ways.

The result is that *all* of us will pick up a variety of general cues from that part of the overarching culture to which we belong, as well as specific cues from the social situation or context in which we find ourselves – learning typically based on both formal and informal imitation – even if from an Alexander Technique point of view what we learn is often associated with unnecessary habitual muscular tensions that adversely affect our breathing, muscular elasticity and movement.

East End boys and West End girls

An obvious instance of the power and significance of the social group in shaping behaviour is the way all the predominantly middle-class young women attending The Royal Ballet School in London's Covent Garden possess a classic ballet look both inside and outside the classroom. As well as the 'pull up' in the torso, and the pushed back, over-straightened neck, another characteristic particularly noticeable is that the students walk with their feet turned out too much. One reason for this is that they have consciously learned through explicit intensive training over many years to rotate the knee and stretch the foot away from the midline of the body. Although that skill enables students to get leg extension when placing or lifting it to the side or rear, it then interferes with efficient forward locomotion as the hip joints work best when used in the direction of the line of travel.

Another, less obvious example, is the way in which many young working-class men of diverse ethnicities in inner east London unconsciously acquire, through role models and peer group pressure in school playgrounds and on the streets, some variation of a jaunty, almost cocky walk as a badge of hyper-masculinity. The head is pulled down on to the neck, the shoulders are pulled up and roll markedly,

Above A female dancer performing turnout

the elbows are unduly flexed, there is an exaggerated bending of the knees and the feet are turned out excessively. Although a very different body technique from that learned by the female ballet students, the male gait is also inefficient in terms of carriage and locomotion and just as damaging to the hip joints. Therein lies a tale of two cultures, East End boys and West End girls.

Left A young man communicating hyper-masculinity

A clean sweep

Traditional forms of learning do not always result in adverse effects on the body. Take for example the practice of sweeping using a short broom made from tiger grass or coconut leaves, a practice found all over the Indian subcontinent and in countries with long-established diaspora communities such as Fiji, Guyana, Mauritius, South Africa and Trinidad. Many young rural and urban working-class girls (and a few boys) have learned through observation and emulation of their elders to place an open hand on the lower back before they begin their task. The weight of the open-handed resting arm accomplishes two things. First, it connects the flexible shoulder joint to the stable pelvic girdle and makes it possible for a forward spiralling bend of the torso from the hip joints, triggering a release of the knees. Second, it counterbalances the weight of the arm that is sweeping, allowing workers to walk forward or backward, their legs and arms coordinated with the head, neck and back for extended periods.

Naturally some people are better at the movement than others. But the overall effect is that many girls and women can work with consummate ease for many hours at a task that most of us would experience as backbreaking.

Words and things

Of course words by themselves cannot do justice to the Alexander Technique. Indeed Aldous Huxley once remarked that providing a verbal description of the experience of improved coordination brought about in his lessons with FM Alexander would be even more difficult than describing the colour red to someone who is colour blind. Another way to express the same idea is that it is impossible to reduce the complex kinaesthetic or proprioceptive information involved in Alexander learning to a verbal code.

Above Two women sweep a section of Goa's Patnem Beach, one demonstrating better coordination than her colleague

So we are obliged to face the fact that there is no ideal language, no simple parallelism between words and reality that does justice to the technique – or indeed anything else for that matter. Nevertheless without words we would be in a very difficult place. It's important to use them in a text, just as they are used in Alexander lessons to supplement the non-verbal, touch-based guidance, albeit with some important caveats.

Kinaesthesia and proprioception

Aristotle is credited with the traditional model of the five senses – sight, hearing, smell, taste and touch. Many other senses are now recognised, including pain (nociception) and the ability to detect differences in temperature (thermoception). But scientists have also long been interested in the human capacity to sense movement. In the mid-16th century the Italian scholar and physician, Julius Caesar Scaliger, referred to the 'sense of locomotion'. Later, in the early part of the 19th century, the Scottish surgeon, anatomist and neurologist, Sir Charles Bell, referred to 'muscle sense'. Over half a century later in 1889, another British scientist, the physiologist and neurologist, Henry Charlton Bastian, suggested that 'kinaesthesia' was a better term for such a sixth sense since some of the sensory information feeding back to the brain derived not simply from muscles but from the tendons, joints and skin.

In 1906, Professor Sir Charles Sherrington, in the ground-breaking The Integrative Action of the Nervous System, proposed a tripartite scheme of 'exteroception', which refers to information from outside the body relayed to the brain via the eyes, ears, mouth, nose and skin; 'interoception', which refers to stimuli from within the body produced by internal organs such as the heart, gastrointestinal tract, and genitourinary system; and 'proprioception', the awareness of body and limb positioning generated through information from joint and muscle receptors, and the mechanisms in the inner ear. For example, if you close your eyes and touch the tip of your nose with the pad of your forefinger or walk in complete darkness without losing balance, you are using the proprioceptive sense. Although Alexander preferred to use the term kinaesthesia to refer to our sense of being in position and movement, many scientists use the terms kinaesthesia and proprioception interchangeably as I shall.

It's evident that Alexander displayed considerable ambivalence about precisely what aspects of his technique it was possible to describe in words without a corresponding hands-on experience. Although in his early writings he had given brief accounts of everyday activities such as sitting and standing, bending and walking, in the 1941 Preface to his third book *The Use of the Self*, he responded to those who had read his books and then wrote to him asking for more practical instruction as (not unreasonably) many readers wanted to know how to 'do' it so they could teach themselves. Alexander denied that he was deliberately withholding information, and warned his readers of his own experience of the danger of trying to 'do it right' by using too much effort whilst reciting. This malcoordination had caused various problems with his throat and nose and jeopardised his career as an actor. Alexander also noted that despite the countless number of books available most people 'are unable to teach themselves to drive a car, play golf, ski or even to master such comparatively simple subjects as geography, history or arithmetic without the aid of a teacher.'

In the same text Alexander took the opportunity to make several additional points about the unique characteristics of his technique.

- The first is to ask the student not to rely on familiar feelings of 'right' and 'wrong' when responding to a stimulus to carry out an action, but instead to reflect and intentionally 'inhibit' or pause. In an Alexander lesson that inhibitory moment allows someone to suspend a habitual response allowing the exploration of different sorts of inputs and experiences in a number of teacher-guided movements such as sitting and standing, bending, going on to the toes or walking. In this way the student learns how not to make too much effort, not only in preparation for but also whilst performing, simple everyday activities.

- A second point is the enormous importance given in the technique to acquiring an on-going, conscious employment of the 'primary control', which according to Alexander, means 'a certain use of the head and neck in relation to the rest of the body'. In a nutshell that involves learning to let the head be lightly poised on the atlas, the top-most vertebra of the spine, while the neck and back muscles which provide support and stability for the head and spine, allow full expansion of the torso. In turn this promotes optimum breathing.

- A crucial point made by Alexander is that an experienced teacher can take a new student to a point in a few weeks that he himself arrived at only after several years of trying to work out a solution to his long-standing voice problem.

Coordination matters

Yet my experience suggests that for this kind of accelerated learning to happen the student has to understand at least something of the problem that has to be solved. Without additional contextual information it is often very difficult for someone to make sense of what has been learnt in lessons in a teaching room and translate it to their everyday activities, such as how to maintain good balance while standing in a slow-moving queue, sitting at a work station, picking up a kettle, using a knife and fork, talking to a family member or friend, running to catch a bus or running a marathon. In short, how people experience life for the far greater amount of time when they are not actually in an Alexander lesson.

In his second book *Constructive Conscious Control of the Individual* Alexander goes at least some way to solving the conundrum by providing a detailed account of a procedure which involves a student sitting upright on a chair facing the back of a second chair equipped with a reasonably high back. Maintaining the balance of the head on the neck the teacher slowly brings the student's body forwards from the hip joints. The student is then instructed to use extended fingers and thumbs to form a beak-like grip with each hand and take hold of the top rail of the chair in front, with the wrists curved inwards and the elbows curved outwards. Once accomplished the teacher (amongst other things) shows the student how to release the elbows outwards and slightly downwards in order to generate a gentle forearm pull or stretch from the fingers and thumbs. If you are not familiar with the procedure it might appear to be rather strange. In fact leaning forwards and then placing the hands on the back of a chair in this way generates a dynamic, elastic muscular release not only in the arms but also in the neck and shoulder girdle, and rib cage and pelvis. It also helps to fine tune your kinaesthetic sense (more on this in Chapter 8).

For most of us, however, performing this series of seemingly simple actions on our own is no easy task. For example, whilst initiating the forward movement towards the chair typically we pull the head down on to the neck so that instead of the torso rotating freely and easily from the hip joints we attempt to use the lower back as a hinge joint and so create a spinal collapse. At the same time we also tighten the muscles of the legs and feet. Then when placing the hands on the rail of the chair we will probably raise the shoulders, further rounding the back and stiffening the chest, arms and hands. Such a muscular muddle! Moreover you can be sure that this pattern of malcoordination is not specific to putting hands over the back of the chair, but will also be evident to a greater or lesser degree in everything you do with your arms and hands irrespective of whether you are bending forwards from the hip joints or not – for example how you thread cotton through the eye of a needle, spread butter on toast, use a mobile phone, operate a computer keyboard, open a jam jar, use a vacuum cleaner, pull a weed from the ground or move a wheelbarrow full of bricks. I tend to agree with Alexander that for the sake of your long-term health and well-being it makes sense for you to learn how to efficiently perform hands over the back of a chair in sitting and standing so that these insights can be applied to almost all your everyday activities.

Alexander was also right to argue that in learning how to use the arms and hands efficiently there is no point in relying on 'physical exercises' of the sort carried out as part of 'physical culture' – nowadays, for example, that would include 'working out' at the gym, performing yoga or Pilates – or various forms of postural training because these activities simply do not address the fundamental and intertwined problems of habitual malcoordination and a faulty kinaesthetic sense that most of us suffer from.

Hands over the back of a chair

Alexander first described hands over the back of a chair in a pamphlet published in 1910. The 1923 version in **Constructive Conscious Control of the Individual** *(referred to as a 'technical evolution') was in part written by Alexander to use copyright law to prevent others from plagiarising his work. But it's also apparent by this time (as I learnt from talking to some of those who trained with Alexander in the 1930s and later on), that putting hands over the back rail of a chair either in sitting or standing was no longer perceived just as an 'exercise' to promote 'robust physical well-being' but an activity that offers important lessons in coordination about how people might best use themselves whilst going about their everyday business. As Alexander noted in his later account of hands over the back of a chair: 'I want it to be very clearly understood that when I write of the arms, legs, hands and feet, etc.,* **I always imply their co-ordinated use** *with the body as a co-ordinated support. Indeed, we might say that in this sense the body represents the trunk of a tree and the arms the limbs.'*

All of us are different and so the instructions given to one student in performing hands over the back of a chair will not be identical to those given to another. Nevertheless Alexander's written account is extremely useful as a reference and starting point. He reckoned that an experienced teacher would be able to use it and 'should be able to supply these instructions in the practical application of the technique to meet the needs of the individual case.' I am following that tradition, except that I have widened the brief considerably to describe many other everyday activities other than the very small number that Alexander wrote about. In doing so this book brings together and explores in some detail aspects of

Above Alexander showing a student how to put hands over the back of a chair

the traditions of some of the main schools of the Alexander Technique, as well as information that I have gleaned from the experience of teaching, and exchanging work with some of my Alexander teacher colleagues.

Learning from hunter-gatherers

Throughout the text I have used many cross-cultural examples of human behaviour. In particular I have made several references to the Hadza people who live in a dry savannah area of north-west Tanzania, near Lake Eyasi, in the Great Rift Valley. Why? Well I consider the Hadza are particularly significant, partly because they have lived continuously in the place where our species *Homo sapiens* first evolved, but mainly because they are one of the last remaining groups of nomadic hunter-gatherers on the planet. Only about 400 or so Hadzas adhere closely to a foraging lifestyle, without recourse to food storage, cultivation or animal husbandry. In the absence of modern technological medicine, juvenile mortality is high (around 45 per cent die by the age of 15), but those who survive to adulthood remain active into their 70s or 80s. Although

by our standards the Hadza have a hard life they do not suffer from cardiovascular disease, obesity or osteoporosis, have excellent eyesight, hearing and teeth, and cancer is more or less unknown. They do not get lower back pain either. Not all contemporary hunter-gatherer peoples are as healthy as the Hadza, however, so we have much to learn from them. Fortunately they have been studied since the late 1950s by social and cultural anthropologists, as well as more recently by medical scientists keen to unlock secrets of their health and well-being.

Above A Hadza man starting a fire

Because their social organisation and culture is certainly different from ancient groups of warm-climate hunter-gatherers the Hadza are not by any stretch of the imagination 'living fossils' as some journalists and travel writers using a catchy phrase have written. Nevertheless even though they are not subject to the same cultural influences as the vast majority of people alive today, the way the Hadza organise aspects of their lives provides important clues to many types of routine activities that *all* humans living in small, multi-aged, socially co-operative mobile groups will have pursued from around 200,000 years ago until the advent of farming and settled communities which began in the Middle East and elsewhere some 12,000 years ago. The Hadza provide examples of ways of using the body which evolved through natural selection, such as standing, going on to the toes, squatting, sitting on the ground, walking and running – interestingly activities which are an important part of contemporary Alexander Technique teaching.

Of course humans the world over by virtue of having big brains and a capacity for using linguistic symbols and creating culture have evolved to do much more than just forage. That means there is little point in simply emulating or reproducing the lifestyles of present-day (or ancient) African hunter-gatherers in an attempt to live healthier happier lives in harmony with 'nature'. To claim that because of our species' history we are ill-suited to modern life is to indulge in what evolutionary biologist Marlene Zuk calls a 'paleofantasy'. In our society in our free time we can learn to play the violin or play golf, listen to the radio or watch TV, go to the cinema or the opera, or ride a bicycle or drive a car – options which are unavailable to the Hadza who find other equally interesting ways of forging social bonds and keeping themselves entertained. Nevertheless it is too easy to throw out the paleo-baby with the paleo-bathwater. Indeed we would be wise to recognise that in many respects the highly active lifestyle of our hunter-gatherer cousins provides an evolutionary benchmark against which we can measure our own. One very big and significant difference between us and the Hadza foragers is that we sit on chairs (badly for the most part) and they do not – at least not yet.

The network society

Alexander was no philosopher, but he was opposed from a practical, functional point of view to body-mind dualism, or indeed any other form of classification which splits the organism into parts. The relevance of this insight is profound. We have all had direct and indirect experience of the tremendous changes that have taken place in recent decades as a result of globalisation and

Above A group of people gathered around and drawn into a screen

the spread of consumer culture. In North America, Europe, Japan and elsewhere, traditional manufacturing, and the manual jobs that have accompanied it, is in decline or largely performed by machines, while the sedentary service sector – the so-called knowledge economy involving the control and manipulation of signs, symbols and people – has increasingly become the motor that drives economic activity and, with it, social and cultural change. For those of us who live in the developed world brain has largely replaced brawn in the world of work. Put another way, livelihoods are made through listening, talking and typing, rather than pulling, pushing and carrying material objects.

The internet and associated technologies are an integral part of this socio-economic transformation. The Spanish sociologist and urbanist Manuel Castells suggests that the innovations which are now taking place are as significant as those which marked the shift from the agrarian to the Industrial Revolution. He is almost certainly right. The development of a global 'network society', in which the way people define themselves and others, is mediated both at work and in leisure time through fast-changing technologies (including those used to generate new digital worlds) is unlike anything that has happened before in human history.

However even if you participate in virtual experiences, and your 'mind' is 'elsewhere' because of a burgeoning techno-utopia, the simple fact is that you still have a 'body'. That body is obliged to operate in a constant gravitational field in real time and space. Much as some people might desire or imagine it there can be no permanent escape from our bodily existence into 'pure' mind, emotion, and spirit – or, indeed, anything else. So although Alexander's discoveries about psycho-physical unity and the effects of good and bad coordination (what he called 'use') on the body's functioning or physiology emerged from a particular tradition of the Western performing arts, some of those insights into our embodiment are as universally applicable and relevant *now* as when he first started teaching his technique to young actors in Auckland and Melbourne in the late 19th century.

Above Technological advances make possible new digital worlds

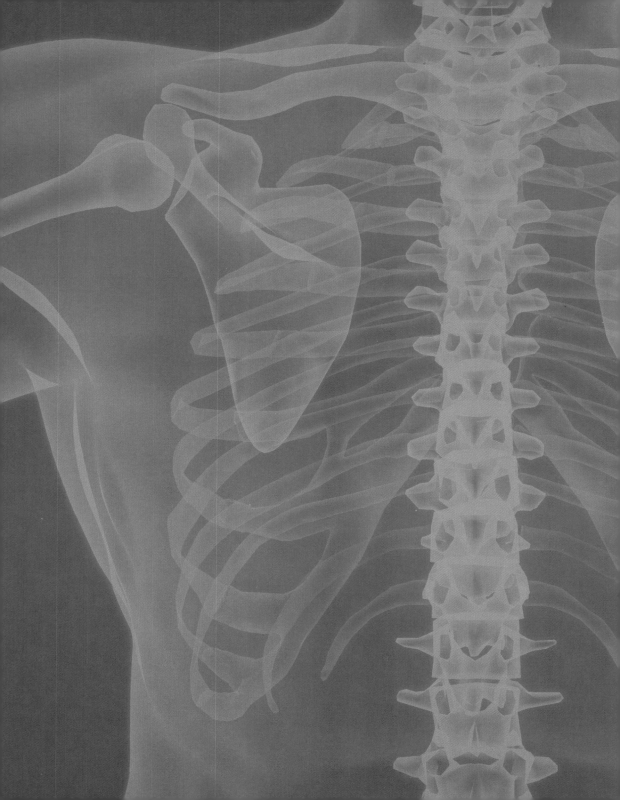

Chapter 2 – *Frederick Matthias Alexander's Discovery*

'The basic discovery Alexander made… was the practice of deliberate conscious inhibition. He stopped doing habitual things seen reflected in the mirror and recognised by him as being wrong: such as pulling his head back when speaking emphatically. He had discovered it to be a useless action. It diminished his standing height, strained his tensing throat; and in particular it interfered with the ease and regularity of his breathing when speaking, reciting and acting, as he wished to do publicly'

Raymond Dart

'Without any outside help Alexander worked out, during a series of agonising years, how to improve what is now called the 'use' of his body musculature in all his postures and movements. And the remarkable outcome was that he regained control of his voice. This story, of perceptiveness, of intelligence, and persistence, shown by a man without medical training, is one of the true epics of medical research and practice'

Nikolaas Tinbergen

In this chapter I have documented Alexander's discovery of the importance of the head, neck and back relationship and its effect on the rest of the body in some detail. In particular I want to convey to you the novel means and extraordinary level of dedication by which he made and then consolidated the discovery concerning the way in which our general coordination affects functioning. It's clear that if Alexander had not discovered his method for improving the way we use ourselves then nothing comparable to the Alexander Technique would exist.

Losing a voice

Frederick Matthias Alexander, known in later life as 'FM' to his students and friends, was born at Table Cape, in rural north-western Tasmania on 20 January, 1869. He was the eldest of 10 children. His parents were the descendants of agricultural labourers in England, sent to Australia after the 1830 'Swing Riots', when threshing machines were destroyed as a protest against food shortages and wage cuts imposed by affluent tenant farmers.

From an early age Alexander took a keen interest in English literature and poetry. He was particularly interested in the plays of Shakespeare and practised reading them aloud to himself, while at the same time attempting to interpret the characters. Growing in confidence Alexander started to perform in public in Melbourne and built something of a reputation. He decided to make the switch from being an amateur to a professional reciter and voice coach.

In 1892 after some years plying his new trade in Melbourne, Alexander began to be plagued by two problems that actors and many other vocal professionals really fear. The first was the development of serious trouble with his throat and vocal cords. The second was that while reciting he was sucking in air, which friends told him was making an unpleasant gasping sound. It's the sort of sound that nowadays can be heard produced by some television and radio newsreaders and presenters. For the most part, they get away with it as long as the vocal delivery is not too loud and is of relatively short duration. But in the acting profession of Alexander's time (and still today for stage actors) it was simply unacceptable from an aesthetic point of view.

Above F M Alexander (1869-1955) as a young actor

As might be expected Alexander's first reaction was to seek the advice of a number of doctors and voice trainers. The diagnosis offered by the medical profession was irritation of the mucous membrane of the throat and nose, as well as inflammation of the vocal cords. Alexander was also told that his uvula, the U-shaped extension of the soft palate that hangs above the tongue, was enlarged and was the reason that he suffered coughing fits. Two of his doctors suggested he undergo an operation to shorten it. He declined.

Alexander was also instructed to follow various treatments, but none of those offered provided a solution. In fact the problem with his voice worsened; on occasion he would lose his voice completely. Not surprisingly he was consumed by doubts about his capacity to continue performing as an actor. Serendipity then presented him with a particularly 'attractive and important engagement', but the question was, should he accept? Alexander decided to consult a physician, Dr Charles Bage, who had previously treated him, to see if anything more could be done.

This time Bage examined Alexander's throat and suggested that he abstain from reciting and to use his voice as little as possible before the engagement. It was a 'rest cure', in other words. Alexander immediately felt reassured. He decided that he would accept the invitation after all. Indeed, his confidence improved when after a few days of rest the hoarseness in his throat disappeared, and his voice returned to normal. When the big night arrived Alexander was in fine form. He started the programme well, but after an hour when he was about halfway through the performance his voice deteriorated. By the end of the evening he could barely speak.

It was evidently a very depressing experience – Alexander realised that his plan to be a great Shakespearean reciter looked as if it might be over. What to do? Once again he consulted his favourite medical adviser, Dr Bage, who advised that treatment should continue. Alexander refused. Bage was evidently puzzled. But Alexander explained that even though he had followed the physician's instructions to the letter, the therapy had failed. Then, using a beautiful piece of logic, he suggested to Bage that it appeared that the vocal problems were not caused by something he was doing prior to the performance, but something he was doing while he was actually performing. Alas, history does not record whether Alexander had already thought of this possibility, or if it was a spur-of-the-moment insight brought about by dialogue with his physician. In any event, Bage agreed with his patient that this indeed might well be the source of the problem, but could not provide any further explanation. 'Very well,' Alexander replied. 'If that is so, I must try and find out for myself.'

Mirror, mirror on the wall

Alexander had two facts to go on. First, ordinary speech did not cause a problem, but recitation, especially when there was a significant demand on the vocal apparatus, did. He calculated that there was something he was doing while he was reciting that was absent in ordinary speaking. He decided to use a long mirror to try and detect differences between the two modes of speaking. (Later on in his experiments he added two more mirrors on either side of the central one.)

It's important to note that at this point in his journey of discovery Alexander knew nothing about anatomy or physiology. For example, he would not have known any of the technical details about where the skull sits on the atlas, the topmost neck vertebra, or the names of the muscles at the front and back of the torso that attach to the back of the skull. In fact that was a great advantage as it would have been all too easy for Alexander to have got bogged down in anatomical and physiological theories of one sort or another, rather than relying on what he could see in the mirrors.

Furthermore, as an actor he had, like many performers, dancers, for example, an inbuilt advantage over most people who use a mirror to look at themselves. In the context of recitation, he would not have been focused primarily on his appearance from a presentational point of view – his hair, his clothing, the presence of facial blemishes and so on – but instead on how he was using or misusing his body in performance. In short, he was looking at his mirror image for information about his general coordination. Naturally left-handed, Alexander will almost certainly have benefited from observing and analysing the bodily quirks and foibles of his right-handed friends and acquaintances.

It was not long before Alexander had worked out that the moment he began to recite there was a tendency to pull back his head, depress his larynx, and suck in air, which produced the gasping sound that he and his friends found so unpleasant. Alexander then re-evaluated what happened in ordinary speech and noticed that the same pattern was evident, except that it was much less pronounced. He had now worked out that the vocal problems were directly linked with how he was using himself – his general coordination.

Working out the puzzle

But Alexander was faced with a serious problem: what was cause and what was effect? There seemed to be three options in relation to making sense of what was going on:

- Was it sucking in breath that caused the pulling back of the head and the depressing of the larynx?

- Was it the pulling back of the head which was causing the depressing of the larynx and the sucking in of breath?

- Was it the depressing of the larynx which was causing the sucking in of breath and the pulling back of the head?

After many months of experimentation Alexander concluded, amongst many other remarkable observations that it was option two that was causal – that is, the pulling back of the head was depressing the larynx and triggering the audible sucking in of air. By now he had also observed that the pulling back of the head was also associated with lifting the chest and shortening the stature by pulling in the middle back.

Additionally he realised that it was not possible to directly control the sucking in of the breath or the depressing of the larynx, but that it was possible to some extent to prevent the pulling back of the head, which stopped the other things happening. That also considerably reduced the problem of hoarseness. It was something of a breakthrough, especially the realisation that his general coordination affected the functioning of the vocal and respiratory mechanisms. This ultimately led Alexander to the discovery of the significance of the 'true primary movement', what he later called the 'primary control' – that is, a coordinated relationship between the neck, the head and the back that allows us to use ourselves more efficiently not only in vocalisation, but in all activities and movements.

The relationship between the head, neck and back – the primary control

Alexander would not have been the first and certainly will not be the last actor to work out that the relationship between the head and neck to vocal production is important. Countless others have found out something similar. For example, five decades after Alexander began his experiments, during filming for the 1944 Hollywood movie *To Have and Have Not*, Betty Bacal, a part-time fashion model, who had appeared on the cover of *Harper's Bazaar*,

Above Lauren Bacall (1924-2014) and 'The Look'

discovered that she could control her nerves and trembling voice if she pressed her chin down towards her chest and looked at the camera with her eyes tilted upwards. Indeed so taken was director Howard Hawks with what Bacal was doing that he encouraged her to carry on. The rest is history. Bacal's head positioning became known as 'The Look', which along with a cultivated, deep husky voice, became very valuable trademarks for the then inexperienced 18-year-old actor, who went on to enjoy considerable fame and fortune as Lauren Bacall.

Alexander's discovery of the primary control was altogether more subtle than Bacall's relatively crude head positioning. In fact in the course of his experiments he attempted something very similar to Bacall when he tilted his head definitely forward, but realised that beyond a certain point he was pulling his head down as well as forward. That too resulted in a shortening of the stature. And the effect on his voice was very similar to when he habitually pulled his head back and down. He concluded that both actions were depressing the larynx. While Bacall could get away with a forward and down head position because she was primarily a screen actor, this was neither possible nor desirable for a reciter such as Alexander, where the demands on vocal performance are far more rigorous and intense.

Legs, feet and toes

Alexander also discovered that his habitual way of vocalisation was linked to other patterns of malcoordination in his body. For example, he began to notice that at the same time as he was interfering in the neck, head and torso, he was also making unnecessary muscular tension in his legs, feet and toes. In fact he was contracting and bending his toes downwards in such a way that he was throwing his weight on to the outside of the foot, creating an arching effect, which, in turn interfered with his overall balance.

It turned out that this pattern of interference in the lower limbs was a response to an expatriate English-born actor and voice teacher, James Faucitt Cathcart, who had instructed a 20-year-old Alexander to 'take hold of the floor' with his feet. Initially, of course, it was a conscious activity, but over time had become part of Alexander's subconscious repertoire in both ordinary speaking and dramatic recitation.

Relying on feeling or thought

So Alexander concluded that his misuse or malcoordination was part of a total pattern. Having established the problem, he now needed to find a solution. The big question: was there one? At this point, I suggest, most people would have been tempted to throw in the towel, and looked to find an alternative way of making a living. However, Alexander refused to believe that the situation was hopeless and kept an open mind, not least because he still had dreams of becoming a great Shakespearean reciter.

Gradually it dawned on Alexander how untrustworthy feeling –'unreliable sensory appreciation' or 'debauched kinaesthesia' as he later called it – was as a guide to remedial action, because he could see in his mirrors that while he *felt* he was putting his head forward and up, it was in *reality* going back and down. There was no doubt about it: whatever he might be 'feeling' was happening, the brutal truth was that he was still depressing his larynx and sucking in breath as he vocalised.

Eventually Alexander gave up trying to 'do' anything and refused to react in a habitual way to his internal stimulus to speak. Instead, he would simply think what he wanted to happen, giving orders or directions for his head, neck and back in front of the mirror for days and months on end – 'to boredom and beyond', as he later described it to one of his students.

Alexander also discovered that it was not sufficient to give the directions before speaking, but it was necessary to continue to give them whilst speaking, even though it felt 'wrong'. That was a huge step in the right direction. In essence Alexander's breakthrough came about because he refused to act immediately on a stimulus – any stimulus – but in his case the stimulus to speak. In short:

- Alexander recognised that he could not rely on his kinaesthetic sense – feelings – as a guide to activity

- He therefore 'inhibited' or refused to make any immediate response to the stimulus to speak a sentence

- While observing himself in the mirror, he gave the 'mental' directions in the proper sequence – neck, head, back and limbs – to maintain lengthening of the stature but not attempting to 'do' anything

- He considered whether to carry out the original action, and then made a fresh decision whether to carry out the activity, do nothing at all, or do something entirely different such as lifting a hand while carrying on giving the directions which would maintain his height

This conscious ability to stop, step back and consider whether to carry out an activity – the practice of inhibition – while maintaining the conscious mental directions to the body, really was the complete breakthrough Alexander had been looking for. It constituted a technique that put an emphasis on the process rather than the goal – what he called, in rather old-fashioned terminology, 'a new means whereby' as opposed to 'end-gaining'. By 1895 not only was Alexander able to vocalise without losing height, narrowing his torso and damaging his vocal apparatus, but the technique he had discovered also allowed him to escape from the on-going throat, nasal and respiratory illnesses, with which he had been plagued since infancy.

Evolution of a teaching technique

Although Alexander initially gave voice lessons using his 'full-chest breathing method' to groups of actors in Australia and New Zealand while on tour, he soon found that it was impossible to convey through words alone what was required. In short, it was not possible to reduce complex kinaesthetic information about what he wanted to convey – the 'means whereby' – to a form of words. As Alexander put it, 'This plan, though simple in theory, has proved difficult for most pupils to put into practice.' At this point he started putting his hands on students in order to convey something of the appropriate kinaesthetic experience that was required to activate a better working of the head, neck and back relationship.

In the course of his experiments in front his mirrors Alexander also saw that his technique had an application to general coordination and movement. He noted, for example, that as he went to sit on a chair in order to rest and reflect many of the same patterns he had noticed in habitual vocalisation, such as pulling his head back and down, shortening his stature, narrowing his back and interfering with his breathing were also made manifest. He realised that the technique did not need to be confined to instructing actors how best to use their voices and breathe, but could be taught in other ways, especially through simple everyday movements.

The gradual shift by Alexander in the late 1890s from a focus on vocal work with *groups* to showing an *individual* how to deal with the 'problem of the control of human reaction', by a guided movement in and out of the chair as well as other procedures, created a new and broader constituency for the technique. Although Alexander maintained an interest in acting all his life, his rapidly-evolving understanding of the implications of the method he had worked out was sufficient to convince him that, despite the widespread critical acclaim his dramatic performances were now gathering, his future lay in teaching.

In Australia Alexander made contact with a number of leading doctors, who were highly intrigued by his discovery, especially because of the indirect effect of an improved head, neck and back relationship on the interrelated musculoskeletal and respiratory systems. One of them, surgeon Dr William J Stewart McKay, of Lewisham Hospital in Sydney, took a course of lessons and impressed by the uniqueness of the technique and the effects on his health, advised Alexander to travel to London, then the centre of an extensive British Empire, to gain a larger audience and a more reliable income stream. To that end McKay wrote letters of introduction for Alexander to some of London's most eminent doctors, whom he knew from medical school.

Leaving Australia for the UK

In April 1904, at the age of 35, Alexander sailed from Melbourne and arrived in London a few weeks later. He never returned to the land of his birth. Although he missed the climate and outdoor life of his homeland, as well as his family and friends, there were compensations to life in the UK as Alexander became something of a celebrity in the upper echelons of British society (and later in the US, where he worked during the First and Second World Wars).

Indeed, his work became quickly recognised and several leading doctors as well as prominent members of the acting profession, including Sir Henry Irving, Oscar Asche, Matheson Lang, Lillie Langtry and Viola Tree, took lessons in the technique. Charging four guineas for a half-hour session (later reduced to three guineas), and giving around 18 lessons a day, Alexander made a very good living. He was a regular visitor to the iconic Café Royal in Regent Street and purchased Penhill, a country house set in 20 acres of gardens and farmland in Bexleyheath, Kent in 1925.

Later on Alexander gave lessons to a number of other prominent people, including authors George Bernard Shaw and Aldous Huxley; Sir Stafford Cripps, Chancellor of the Exchequer in Clement Attlee's post-Second World War Labour government; Columbia University's Professor John Dewey, a leading light in the American pragmatist school of philosophy; Henry Cotton, winner of three Open Championships; chocolatier and philanthropist Joseph Rowntree; and Clementine Churchill. Alexander also received support for his method from the UK-born 1932 Nobel prize winner for Physiology or Medicine, Professor Sir Charles Sherrington; the US anatomist Professor George E Coghill; and Australian-born neuroanatomist and palaeoanthropologist, Professor Raymond Dart (who took a course of Alexander lessons in Johannesburg from Irene Tasker, one of Alexander's earliest apprentices, as well as a single lesson from Alexander, on a visit to London in 1949).

Above Henry Cotton (1907-1987), one of Alexander's students

In 1931, after considerable pressure from his supporters, including leading ophthalmologist Andrew Rugg-Gunn and physicians Andrew Murdoch and Peter Macdonald, who were extremely concerned that the technique might disappear with the death of the founder, Alexander and a handful of his apprentices then opened an intensive three-year course for students – extended to four years for the first cohort – at his practice at Ashley Place in London's Victoria. Apart from the war years, the training course carried on until Alexander's death in London on 10 October 1955. Remarkably, Alexander was still giving eight lessons a day until a week or so before he passed away.

The globalisation of the Alexander Technique

Since its founder's death the Alexander Technique has spread globally. The Society of the Teachers of the Alexander Technique (STAT) was established in the UK in 1958, and a number of affiliated societies in countries in Europe, North America, South America, Africa, Australasia and the Middle East have been established, mainly by teachers who originally trained in London. These local societies approve and regulate Alexander Technique teacher training courses.

A kinaesthetic learning approach to health and well-being

Although when he first arrived in the UK Alexander was known as the 'The Breathing Man', because of his expertise in vocalisation and the respiratory system, the types of problems with which people sought help from him or were referred by doctors were extraordinarily varied. His students included those suffering from asthma, anxiety, depression, epilepsy, hypertension, insomnia, locomotor ataxia, migraine, nasal and throat problems, neurasthenia (now called chronic fatigue syndrome or ME), osteoarthritis, Parkinson's disease, polio, sciatica, scoliosis, 'shell shock' or post-traumatic stress disorder (after World War I), short-sightedness, stuttering, spasmodic torticollis, sports injuries, trigeminal neuralgia, visceroptosis and conditions caused by accidents of one sort or another. Of course Alexander also gave lessons to those not suffering from any illness or malady, but had read his books or had been recommended to have lessons by other students of the technique and who were keen to explore the 'use of the self'. Lessons were also given to children suffering from learning difficulties, and a small-scale school was established in 1924 for them.

Alexander and his followers have always been very careful not to categorise the technique as a type of alternative or complementary medicine that aims to 'cure' using direct means or treatments. Instead it is best viewed as kinaesthetic learning, which has indirect benefits for health and well-being brought about by an improvement in general coordination.

Nobel Prize winner endorses the Alexander Technique

A significant milestone in raising the international profile of the Alexander Technique was achieved when Nikolaas Tinbergen, Professor of Animal Behaviour at the University of Oxford, along with Karl von Frisch and Konrad Lorenz, were awarded, the Nobel Prize in Physiology or Medicine in 1973. In his acceptance speech *Ethology and Stress Diseases* given at the Karolinska Hospital in Stockholm, Dutch-born Tinbergen paid tribute to Alexander, especially his method of 'watching and wondering' what he was doing with his body as he spoke in front of the mirrors. That, Tinbergen thought, was similar in some ways to the observational and analytical techniques employed by animal behaviourists.

He recounted that, along with his wife and one of his daughters, he had undertaken a course of lessons in the technique after reading Dr Barlow's *The Alexander Principle*. In a succinct summary of what's involved Tinbergen told his audience that the method 'is based on

Above Nobel prize-winning animal behaviourist and champion of the Alexander Technique, Nikolaas Tinbergen (1907-1988)

exceptionally sophisticated observation, not only by means of vision but also to a surprising extent by using the sense of touch. It consists in essence of no more than a very gentle, first exploratory, and then corrective manipulation of the entire muscular system.' Tinbergen added that he could 'already confirm some of the seemingly fantastic claims made by Alexander and his followers, namely, that many types of under-performance and even ailments, both mental and physical, can be alleviated, sometimes to a surprising extent, by teaching the body musculature to function differently.'

Recent research on the Alexander Technique

The Alexander Technique has been the subject of scientific research at a number of leading UK, US and Australian universities. Studies include the technique's application to breathing problems, dysfunctional movement patterns, chronic back pain, chronic neck pain, Parkinson's disease, and the implications for psychological health and well-being through touch.

The largest scientific study to date was carried out in the UK by a team of researchers led by Paul Little, Professor of Primary Care Research in the Faculty of Medicine at the University of Southampton. It involved 579 patients suffering from chronic or recurrent lower back pain, a common source of disability and absence from work. The condition affects around seven out of 10 people in modern sedentary societies at some time in their lives.

Building on previous research which showed that 'the practice and theory of the technique, in conjunction with preliminary findings of changes in postural tone and its dynamic adaptability to changes in load and position, support the hypothesis that the technique could potentially reduce back pain by limiting muscle spasm, strengthening postural muscles, improving coordination and flexibility, and decompressing the spine'. The results of the randomised trial were impressive; 'I had a pretty good suspicion that people who were well-motivated would do well with the technique,' commented Professor Little when the research was published in the *British Medical Journal* in 2008. 'But you have to be committed to learning it for it to benefit you. I suspected most folks might not be that committed and so we might not show terribly much.' Significantly, he added: 'This is a good, large trial. It is good enough evidence for people to take it seriously.'

The Alexander Technique lessons, exercise, and massage study (ATEAM) for chronic and recurrent back pain was carried out by researchers led by Professor Paul Little at the universities of Southampton and Bristol. The results were published in the British Medical Journal in August 2008. Subjects suffering with chronic or recurrent lower back pain were recruited from 64 GP practices across the South and West of England. In the trial, 144 patients were randomly allocated to normal GP care, 147 to six sessions of classic massage, 144 to six, and another 144 to 24 one-to-one lessons in the Alexander Technique using 'manipulation and verbal instruction' to 'improve musculoskeletal use when stationary and in movement' by experienced teachers belonging to the Society of Teachers of the Alexander Technique (STAT). Half of each group were also randomly selected to include a programme of aerobic exercise, which typically involved unsupervised walking. Those in the GP care group acted as controls for the other groups of patients.

The results of the trial were very revealing. Although one subject thought that their back pain had been made worse by massage, no adverse events were reported for either those performing aerobic exercise or those receiving lessons in the Alexander Technique. Overall, although massage was useful in the short term and exercise combined with behavioural counselling 'provided modest but useful benefits', the best outcomes were achieved by the two Alexander groups. Compared with those in the control group, patients who had six Alexander lessons had a 17 per cent reduction in the Roland disability score and a 48 per cent reduction in days in pain, while those who received 24 Alexander lessons, achieved a 42 per cent reduction in the Roland disability score and an 86 per cent reduction in days in pain.

The Alexander Technique has so much more to offer than just the prevention of back pain and other musculoskeletal conditions. It is, as Alexander put it, concerned with how we use ourselves in the myriad activities of our lives using inhibition and direction. The subject of our next chapter.

Above Alexander working with a student

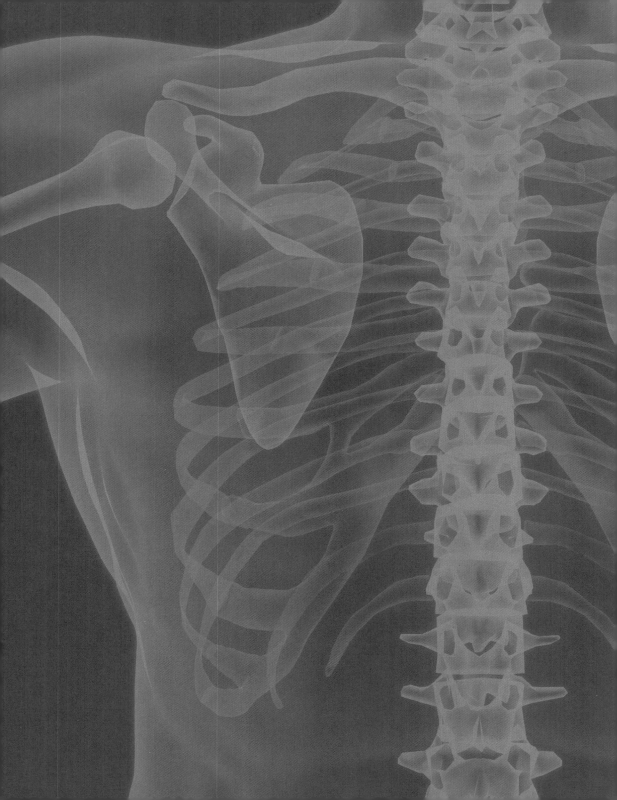

Chapter 3 – *Thinking In Activity*

'We think it reasonable to assume that all humans are endowed with a self-consciousness of mind and body, with an internal body image, and with what neurologists have identified as the proprioceptive or "sixth sense", our sense of body self-awareness, of mind/body integration, and of being-in-the-world as separate and apart from other human beings'

Nancy Scheper-Hughes and Margaret M Lock

'We already notice, with growing amazement, very striking improvements in such diverse things as high blood pressure, breathing, depth of sleep, overall cheerfulness and mental alertness, resilience against outside pressures, and also in such a refined skill as playing a stringed instrument ... Although no one would claim that the Alexander treatment is a cure-all in every case, there can be no doubt that it often does have profound and beneficial effects ... both in the 'mental' and 'somatic' sphere'

Nikolaas Tinbergen

This is a key chapter in understanding what the Alexander Technique is about. I need to say quite a lot and you need to be brave and read it all!

Faulty kinaesthesia

One important point to remember from Alexander's experiments detailed in the previous chapter is that while initially he did all sorts of things – actively putting his head forward and up while widening his back, for example – he came to realise that *doing* anything with different parts of his body did not get to the root of his vocal problem in either dramatic recitation or, as he later spotted, in ordinary conversation. We also saw that Alexander had direct experience of the untrustworthiness of his sensory apparatus because he could see in the mirrors that he was stiffening his neck, rotating his head back and down, lifting his chest and narrowing his back in order to vocalise, even though he *felt* the opposite was happening.

As a result Alexander understood that any novel sensory experience, even an improved one, will often feel markedly different in terms of habitual perceptions of position and movement. He said: 'Obviously, any new use must feel different from the old, and if the old use felt right, the new use was bound to feel wrong.' This means that anyone with 'faulty sensory appreciation' interested in performing an activity with better coordination should not use 'feeling' as a guide – at least until the reliability of the kinaesthetic or proprioceptive sense has sufficiently improved. Indeed, after many false starts Alexander found that he had to trust what he termed his 'reasoning' process – that is, employing conscious inhibition (non-doing) and the projection of mental directions that he had worked out while performing in front of the mirrors.

Learning the Alexander Technique

From a practical point of view what does the concept of faulty sensory appreciation mean? Most students experience pleasant effects both during and after lessons in the Alexander Technique. As a better working primary control is achieved, resulting in a more appropriate balance between the body's extensor and flexor muscles, many report that they feel lighter, more relaxed, more energised, can breathe more easily and are in a better mood. Most will be a different shape and some will be markedly taller, at least for a while.

A minority of people, however, especially the morning after the initial lessons, will ache or feel a degree of mild discomfort or even fatigue, as if they have been involved in some fairly vigorous exercise. This experience often comes as a surprise to a student because the amount of 'physical' activity in a lesson – getting in and out of a chair a few times and a period of lying down – is often fairly limited. But the release of often atrophied muscles into length, especially the large, powerful extensor or anti-gravity muscles of the torso, both during the lesson and for a period afterwards, means that the amount of activity going on in the body may well increase significantly. That sensation of achiness will typically fade after a few lessons as familiarity with the process and a better level of neuromuscular integration takes place.

It's inevitable that some students will at least initially judge some kinaesthetic changes negatively. 'That feels really weird,' students have sometimes said to me after they have rolled off the table at the end of a lesson. Once again this tends to occur early on in a course of lessons (or if someone has not had a lesson for some time) when novel and significant changes in the way someone is standing, sitting or bending have been brought about. Those changes can have a big impact on someone's kinaesthetic sense. For example, when the head goes forward and up, and the spine lengthens, the musculature of the trunk is working more efficiently, yet many people have the experience that they are leaning forward from the hip joints. In actual fact what has happened is that the amount of curvature in the spine has decreased and the pelvis has come back in space – the student is objectively 'straighter' in other words – but from a subjective point of view she might feel not only different but 'out of shape', unsure as this does not feel 'normal'.

Something similar also happens in those students who, for one reason or another, not only shorten the stature but also habitually lean or twist to the left or right. When lengthening of the stature takes place, someone who normally leans, say, to the left will typically feel that they are now leaning to the right and are no longer vertical. Naturally enough they too want to get back to 'normal'. Although understandable, this is an example of a faulty kinaesthetic sense.

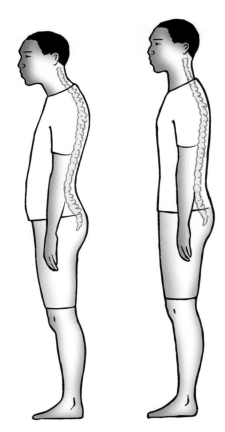

Above Many of us subconsciously pull the head back and down and push the neck forward and down, which results in arching the back and distorting the pelvis and the legs Instead, we need to think consciously of the head being freely poised, the back lengthening and widening, and the cervical and lumbar parts of the spine releasing up and back

Another aspect of the Alexander Technique that some new students can find especially disconcerting occurs when there is a release of some of the excessive contraction of the muscles which attach to and pull the head back (or forward) and down and push the column of the neck forward. Now that the head is releasing forward and up, and the neck is releasing up and back, the student will often feel that she is looking 'down' because the muscles that control the eyes are still 'locked' to the habitual contraction of the neck muscles. In this instance the important thing to realise is that the sensation is only temporary and will disappear once the eyes have learned to work in association with an improved use of the primary control.

A picture is worth a thousand words

To get across the significance of a faulty kinaesthetic sense I think it is a good idea for students to be shown in a mirror that what they feel is going on does not correspond to objective reality. That often creates the space for someone to suspend judgement about what is right and wrong and allow something new to happen.

Sometimes at the beginning of a course of lessons I will ask a student whether, using their smartphone, they would like me to take a picture of their habitual way of standing, and then after a few movements in and out of the chair another image so that a record of what has just taken place can be kept. (I sometimes offer to take a third picture at the end of a lesson.) Although not a perfect methodology, because the representations are static, the binary-type changes involved in going from shortening to lengthening of the stature are often quite dramatic, providing much food for thought. 'I couldn't believe the difference in the "before" and "after" pictures,' a 26-year-old woman recently emailed me after her first lesson. 'It's quite fascinating to see such an improvement in shape in such a short space of time.'

Alexander Technique and the emotions

Of course the way English speakers use the word 'feeling' is not only as a synonym for proprioception. It's also used to describe bodily sensations such as hunger or thirst ('I feel like something to eat' or 'I feel like a drink') and it is to the complex social, cultural, psychological and physiological processes we call 'emotions' to which we now turn.

It's perhaps not surprising that because all of us are consciously 'moved', to a greater or lesser extent, in the course of our everyday lives, that Charles Darwin would claim in his 1872 book *The Expression of the Emotions in Man and Animals* that emotions and their expression in humans overlap with those of other creatures. For example, he thought that the capacity for laughter, once thought of as uniquely human, would have been displayed by a common ancestor of contemporary primates, as 'very many kinds of monkeys, when pleased, utter a reiterated sound, clearly analogous to our laughter, often accompanied by vibratory movements of their jaws or lips, with the corners of the mouth drawn backwards and upwards, by the wrinkling of the cheeks, and even by the brightening of the eyes'. He also observed that young chimpanzees when tickled, especially under the armpits, behave very similarly to children, sometimes emitting 'a chuckling or laughing sound'. In short, according to Darwin the emotions of modern humans are deeply rooted – universal and innate, or biologically determined.

Above Interplay between members of two primate species creates smiles and laughter for both

In the intervening years, however, social and cultural anthropologists have discovered that emotions such as love/ hate, happiness/sadness, empathy/hostility, interest/boredom, optimism/pessimism, and compassion/cruelty are not spread equally, nor do they work in the same way in all societies.

While some emotions such as disgust, fear, happiness, sadness and surprise appear to be universal, others are specific. Take, for example, the intense feeling of pride that many people feel when they hear their country's national anthem, or see the national flag being raised. To those involved the feeling is a given, entirely 'natural', yet that response is peculiar to the citizens of modern nation states. It has no meaning or significance for, say, semi-nomadic pastoralists such as the Maasai, who, with their highly-prized cattle, follow seasonal rains as they have done for centuries, crossing the national boundaries of Tanzania and Kenya.

Similarly with aggression, which many people in the Western world might believe is something that is simply part of 'human nature'. Surprising as it may seem, there are many small-scale societies, such as the Chewong hunter-gatherers, who live in the tropical rainforest of Peninsular Malaysia, where the expression of anger amongst adults as we understand it is unheard of. Though, interestingly, feeling fearful of the unknown and what cannot be controlled, which Westerners tend to regard negatively, is perceived as a positive emotion, and considered to be the essence of being truly human.

Above A Maasai woman and her children sitting in a very balanced way

Also, while concepts of honour and shame seem to be at the heart of nearly all encounters in all societies, a sense of 'embarrassment' seems to be much more significant in Anglo-American cultures which place a particularly high value on individualism and individual expression. The key point here is to recognise that all emotions, universal or specific, are experienced, expressed, shaped and transformed through the mind-bodies of the members of groups within a particular society, or subset of that society.

Nevertheless there is one mechanism that we all use to cope with unwelcome thoughts and emotions regardless of which particular society we belong to – that is, tightening the musculature. A good example is provided by members of the British upper classes who have been famous since the Victorian era for 'keeping a stiff upper lip', especially in times of crisis for fear of being seen to lose self (and group) control. According to the writer and historian A N Wilson 'the greatest factors in the development of the stiff upper lip were English public schools and Scottish Presbyterianism'. He is probably right.

Above The ideological-emotional motif of upper class British men and women

The expression of control and restraint through the body is not peculiar to upper-class British men and women. Indeed something very similar happens amongst the young men of the Samburu people, a group of east African semi-nomadic pastoralists, neighbours of the Maasai, when they undergo circumcision without anaesthetic as part of a four-day initiation ritual marking the transition from childhood to adulthood. After tribal male elders pour a mixture of milk and water over a boy's body to instil ritual purity, an initiate is expected not to flinch or shed tears as the knife used by a high-ranking specialist removes the foreskin. To do so would bring great shame not only on the individual but also to his extended family.

In these examples it is evident that individual experience and 'feelings' are strongly shaped by the relatively 'closed' customary behaviours of two very different social groups. Yet whatever socio-cultural dynamic is in play it is almost impossible to eliminate visible emotional responses through muscular tightening and restricted breathing. Indeed signs of inner turmoil or passion will be evident, as Darwin astutely observed, in the face and eyes of those involved.

Above A group of young Samburu warriors

That's true of even the most stoical upper class, aristocratic or Royal British man or woman at times of genuine sadness and tragedy, or the young Samburu initiate who is expected to experience excruciating pain without overt emotional display on his way to becoming a man and a warrior.

Despite the possibly unique emphasis placed on the pursuit of emotional authenticity in contemporary middle-class Anglo-American culture, be aware that the Alexander Technique does not work or engage *directly* with emotional processes, or how they affect your relationship to other people, either in your private life or at work. Instead the technique is first and foremost concerned with improving your general coordination and proprioceptive sense. That, according to Alexander, is our fundamental challenge. Partly for that reason he was critical of psychoanalysis (and, by extension, what are today called 'talking' therapies) because disentangling the unconscious elements of the past that influence (or distort) people's current mental lives and relationships using words pays insufficient attention to the reality of body-mind functioning. That is self-evidently true. For example, an illuminating insight into your mind, emotions or therapeutic relationship derived from psychoanalysis will not *by itself* change a habitual pattern of malcoordination or a faulty muscle sense. Which when you think about it is odd considering how in our culture emotions are so often expressed or accompanied by gestures of one sort or another – when you either make or avoid eye contact, smile or frown, embrace or turn your back on someone, for instance. Psychoanalysis and similar therapies are undoubtedly kinaesthetically under developed.

In our abstract, fragmented society, however, people often have complex backgrounds and live complex lives. We are social animals and in our culture, in the absence of powerful collective rituals and other forms of non-verbal support available in many traditional societies, we sometimes feel the need to talk about problems and issues with others. Be aware though that if there is a significant or disturbing emotional or other problem in your life to work through, your Alexander Technique teacher is not the best person to solve it. Instead, family and friends, medical or psychological professionals or other experts would be more able to provide the appropriate support or guidance.

All that said, the Alexander Technique is not involved in suppressing emotions, not least because even though we often find them very hard to define (' I'm only going on my gut feelings …') we know from social and biological anthropology the significant role they play in social bonding, while psychology has revealed the crucial role of feelings in motivating us to act the way we do (otherwise we would be robots), and psychoneuroimmunology has uncovered the effect of positive and negative emotional states on the nervous and immune systems

Above Emotions play an important role in social bonding

(you are more likely to catch a cold if you are feeling anxious, hostile or depressed, for example).

Yet whatever your past experience the purpose of an Alexander lesson is for you to come into the present moment. In this way you will learn a better level of neurophysiological integration, in particular improving the balance of your head on your neck and your contact with the floor. This change in your coordination and relationship to gravity is likely to have a positive impact on your sense of body-self – you will feel more comfortable in your skin – and may also, depending on circumstances, allow you to experience, process and then express your feelings to other people in an open and expansive way rather than repressing them.

An improved kinaesthetic sense will also mean that you become aware of inappropriate holding of the musculature – for example, tightening your throat, chest, abdominal or gluteal muscles, stiffening your arms and hands or raising your shoulders. These perhaps might be triggered as a defensive, ad hoc response to an emotionally traumatic past event which has become an integral part of your behavioural repertoire, or because of a stressful on-going event (especially difficult or awkward face-to-face encounters), or because of the influence

Above Rage against the machine

of social or cultural pressures. You then have a chance of releasing them by attending to the integrity of the relationship between your head, neck and back. This is no easy endeavour and for a variety of reasons some people will find this process more difficult to engage with than others. Nevertheless in broad terms the Alexander Technique has important implications in terms of the interaction between your mind and your muscle over and above the acquisition of biomechanically efficient everyday movements. In short, it offers a unique but *indirect* perspective on the role emotions play in your life through your becoming aware of the way in which they are actually embodied as you respond or react to different people and situations. Which brings us neatly to the concepts of inhibition and direction.

Inhibition – *How inhibition works*

When Alexander was exploring the logic of his situation in front of the mirrors and decided not to carry out his intention to speak, he was exercising what he later discovered was called the inhibitory or 'non-doing' part of the nervous system, which is inextricably linked with the excitatory or 'doing' part.

I must emphasise that inhibition as taught in the technique is not primarily concerned with saying 'no' to the physical aspect of a movement. Instead, it is saying 'no' to the *thought* of movement. There is a time and space between any 'internal' or 'external' stimulus – and the type of response that we make in the brain and central nervous system *before* our muscular machinery is activated. In practical terms you are paying particular attention to the relationship between head, neck and back before deciding whether to act or not. Alexander once summarised the significance of the inhibitory process in this way: 'If I ask a pupil to put his arm up, and for five minutes he refuses to give consent, he will be doing as much for his central nervous system as it is possible to do.'

It's also worth noting that the term inhibition as used in the technique is derived from the writings of Sir Charles Sherrington, one of Alexander's supporters, who laid the foundations of modern neurology and neuroscience. Through experimentation with cats, dogs, monkeys and apes, Sherrington discovered the primary significance of the working of the brain and central nervous system and how it affects secondary muscular functioning, including the anti-gravity musculature, as a reflex activity in mammals.

Sherrington viewed excitation and inhibition as complementary. As he explained: 'The whole quantitative grading of the operations of the spinal cord and brain appears to rest upon mutual interaction between the two central processes "excitation" and "inhibition", the one no less important than the other.' Alexander, by contrast, placed a greater emphasis on learning *conscious* inhibition as a specific human skill that *precedes* activity. As he neatly explained: 'My technique is based on inhibition, the inhibition of undesirable, unwanted responses to stimuli, and hence it is primarily a technique for the development of the control of human reaction.'

Whatever the differences between Sherrington and Alexander in the way in which they evaluated the significance of inhibition, both use the concept quite differently from that linked to repression associated with emotions such as anxiety, fear and helplessness popularised by Sigmund Freud, the founder of psychoanalysis.

Now let's explore the meaning and significance of the various Alexander directions.

Above Professor Sir Charles Sherrington (1857-1952) revolutionised the study of neurology and neurophysiology

The Alexander directions – *The primary control*

Like other primates humans have a particularly well-developed visual sense. This harks back to the way our early upright ancestors scanned foreground, middle ground, horizon and sky to detect the presence of prey, anticipate potential danger or interpret changing weather conditions or the position of the sun and moon. Sometimes this information would have triggered immediate action, but at other times it would have prompted reflection and the weighing up of options about the best way to proceed. It's also worth noting that perceptions of the outside world processed through specialist cells in our forward-facing eyes, and relayed deep into the brain, have an enormous influence on our sense of uprightness while standing stationary or in movement.

Yet using our eyes properly to decipher complex three-dimensional fields is a skill that most of us who spend a lot of time reading books or manipulating signs and symbols on computer screens, or daydreaming, have lost, to a greater or lesser extent. It's something we need to restore. Indeed, in the Alexander Technique it is important to initially look out to see something irrespective of whether you are receiving hands on guidance in a lesson, or whilst performing everyday activities. Once engaged your eyes should remain alert and attentive and free to move to take in the environment – what's in front, what's to the sides, what's above and what's below you. Then you can begin directing.

The directions need to be given in a specific order allowing a release of unnecessary tension in your body. Improved general coordination, as Alexander often pointed out, should take place 'from the head downwards' so that partial patterns are always subordinate to the total pattern. Put another way, the relativity of your head to your neck and torso is crucial in activating muscle tone and organising movement throughout the rest of your body. (It's interesting that during labour most of us, with help and encouragement from our mothers, successfully navigated the birth canal with our rotating head leading and a twisting body following.)

From a practical point of view that means that if you become aware that you are interfering with, for example, your feet, ankles, knees, hips, elbows or hands you should give the directions for your head, neck and back *before* adding on directions for the other relevant body part or parts. Although it is certainly possible to direct in reverse, say, from your feet up – or indeed

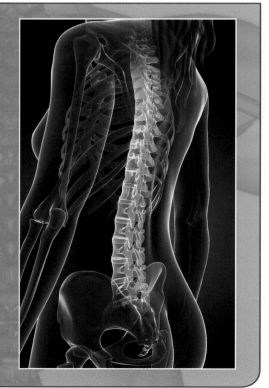

The four curves of the human spine, a structure unique among primates that facilitates efficient bipedal standing and locomotion, consists of an assembly of 33 individual vertebrae. Anatomists conventionally make a distinction, based on shape, between the cervical (seven vertebrae), thoracic (12 vertebrae), lumbar (five vertebrae), sacral (five fused vertebrae), and coccygeal (four fused vertebrae) sections of the vertebral column. The spine is a weight-bearing structure that creates an axis for the human body, with the skull, rib cage, legs and arms best viewed as appendages. The spinal canal houses and protects the spinal cord.

The 24 articulating vertebrae of the spine (cervical, thoracic and lumbar), separated by 23 cartilaginous discs, individually provide some but not much flexibility. Working as a combined unit, however, these joints provide for the possibility of a much greater degree of movement. In turn, the flexibility of the whole spinal column establishes the basis for a sophisticated refinement in balance, and together with the movable joints of the knees, hips and ankles, allows any combination of forward, backward or sideways twisting motions. Additional stabilisation of the spine is brought about by the action of the muscles and ligaments around the vertebrae.

in any order – and create a tangible effect in your body the danger is that, in the words of John Dewey, you will end up with 'a different form of badly'. In short, if you suffer from malcoordination it is only by getting the primary control to work before giving orders for your limbs or other body parts that it is possible to achieve optimum neurophysiological integration.

The three principal directions or orders for the primary control are:

- **Let the neck be free**

  Irrespective of what's going on in your body you should always start with a direction to release any excess tension in the muscles of your neck that attach to the back of your skull. In fact you want to achieve lengthening and elasticity not only in the large external muscles which attach to the back of your head, such as the erector spinae, trapezius and sternocleidomastoid muscles, but also in the smaller internal suboccipital muscles that lie at the junction between the neck and skull. The potential cascading release of tension brought about by this primary direction will help normalise any discrepancies in the four curves of your spine and facilitate delicate tilting and rotatory movements of your head on the topmost joint of your neck, called the atlanto-occipital joint.

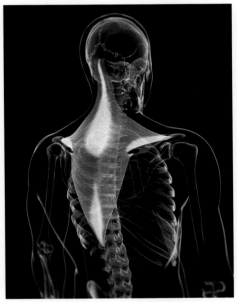

Above The trapezius is one of a set of muscles that attaches to the back of the skull

- **To let the head go forward and up**

  Your head weighs somewhere between 10 and 14 pounds, about eight per cent of body weight. Importantly around two thirds of your head's weight lies in front of its support point, the atlanto-occipital joint, and only one third behind. The result is that the centre of gravity of your head is positioned considerably forward of this support point. In someone who is well-coordinated the head is kept in balance by the stretch mechanism within the muscles that run from the back of the head (occiput) down the full length of the spine. Often, however, we actively tighten these muscles and pull our heads down on to our necks. In doing so, we inadvertently create compression throughout the body.

Your head will readily go forward and up if you give permission for the neck muscles attached to the back of your skull to un-grip and lengthen. It's important to understand, however, that the direction 'head to go forward and up' is only a thought and so does not result in, or end up as, a fixed position. The intention is for your head to maintain a dynamic equilibrium, poised and on the verge of movement so that you can look straight ahead, down at the ground, up at the sky, as well as behind you – as long as it is releasing up and off the top of your spine, all the while supported by the rest of the body's musculature from the feet upwards. It's also worth noting that there is no 'neutral' position for your head, as the neck muscles are tightening by default or releasing into length by intention, unless, of course, it is fully supported – for example, when its weight is given to a pile of books in Alexander lying down. We cover this in Chapter 9.

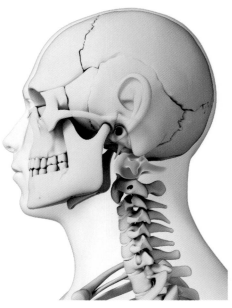

Above Illustration of the atlanto-occipital joint

● **To let the spine lengthen and back widen**
When you consciously release your neck muscles and allow your head to go forward and up, there will be an energising and straightening of the neck and the rest of the spine, generating more 'up' throughout your body. Although we often think of the neck as a distinct entity, in reality it is simply a word for the topmost seven cervical vertebrae and an integral part of the whole length of the 32 spinal vertebrae. When the lengthening of your spine occurs, it happens because both your torso's extensor musculature at the back and the flexors at the front have unclenched and released into elastic length and width. That has a direct and immediate effect on the flexibility and movement of your rib cage, and results in more open breathing.

Most of our skeletal muscles are made up of an equal proportion of two types of fibre – red (slow-twitch) or white (fast-twitch). These fibres have different properties. Red fibres can only contract slowly but are non-fatigable. By contrast, white fibres are able to contract quickly but

Above A man riding a camel on Jumeirah Beach in Dubai

tire easily. The anti-gravity muscles of your back and many of those in your lower legs have evolved to contain a greater proportion of red than white fibres, an adaptation which allows you to maintain uprightness at minimal energy cost. If you habitually collapse your spine, however, the result is that you will lose the ability to deploy these non-tiring support muscles and your ability to perform everyday activities such as standing and un-supported sitting, and endurance activities such as long-distance walking, running, cycling and swimming will be severely compromised.

Another thing to bear in mind is that because many of us have a tendency to think of the lengthening of the spine and widening of the back in only two-dimensions, we mistakenly try to consciously or unconsciously keep the upper body still. This habit only leads to tightening, and interferes with activities such as walking and running, or reaching for an object, all of which should involve efficient twisting or turning around the spinal axis. In short, rather than thinking in only two-dimensions, you need to direct three-dimensionally, so that the contra-rotations in your body are able to work unhindered. We will discuss this issue in more detail in Chapters 5 and 10.

Along with other primates we frequently use a seated attitude in which the spine is vertically-oriented for resting, socialising and feeding. To sit upright efficiently we need to use our sitting bones (ischial tuberosities) and our non-tiring support muscles so that the weight of the head, upper body and arms is transferred into whatever support surface is available. This could be the ground itself, or a raised surface such as a chair, tree stump or rock, or a moving surface such as a horse, elephant or camel.

An easy way for you to locate your sitting bones is to sit on a flat surface such as the floor or a chair and put a hand under each buttock. Through the skin, fatty tissue and thick muscle you will feel a bony protuberance under each hand. Now let yourself slump so that your spine assumes a C-shaped curve. You will notice how you roll on to the back edge of your sitting bones and your weight transfers on to the rear of the pelvis and towards the tail-bone (coccyx). Now try sitting up 'straight' as if you were performing 'good posture'. By arching your back you will experience how your contact moves on to the very front edge of your sitting bones, almost lifting them off the support surface, so that much of your weight is taken by your thighs. By contrast, if you are sitting in balance your weight is taken more or less by the middle of the curved arch of your sitting bones. We return to this subject in Chapter 6.

Right The bones of the pelvis allow us to sit efficiently

The Legs

The limbs have reciprocal relationship with the primary control. So you will need to add on other directions as appropriate. The most important one is:

- **Let the knees go forward and away**
  The direction 'knees to go forward and away' means that your
  upper legs will release forward and outward from your hip joints and slightly away from
  each other. Many of us think that the hips are much higher than they actually are, possibly
  because we confuse the actual hip joints with hip measurement around the area where
  the belt line sits. In fact you can very easily locate the hip joints themselves by placing your
  index fingers, at the very top of each leg in the groin, about a hands breadth across the
  midline, and maintaining the contact, as you sit and stand. In that way, you will be able to
  feel the ball and socket (acetabulofemoral) joints working.

Of course the muscles, ligaments, and tendons directly involved with the hip joints are not the only ones to release when the order knees to go forward and away is given. That releasing direction will involve the whole musculature of your pelvic girdle as well as that of the lower and middle back, around the lowest part of the rib cage, and so creating a spiralling muscular length along your thigh bones (femurs) towards the knees extending right down the lower legs (tibia and fibula bones) to your ankle joints and platforms of the feet. The anatomical significance of the direction of the knees going forward and away from the hip joints and lower back is that it commands the pelvic girdle, and the length of the spine, to work as one connected-up unit, with no false or imaginary moveable joint in the lumbar region of the lower back. The result is that the point of pivoting movement of your torso is then accurately positioned at the top of your legs, at the hip joints.

The shorthand direction of knees forward and away is self-evidently relevant to a wide range of activities where your knee is flexed. That includes sitting on a chair or on the ground, getting out of a chair, squatting, walking, running, riding a bike or horse, driving a car, skiing, roller skating, dancing and Alexander lying down. However even if you are standing still – talking to someone in the office or waiting for a bus, for example – the order is also for your knees to release forward and away. That direction is to prevent

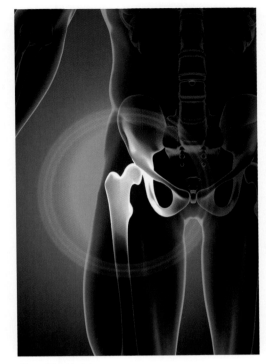

Above The hip joint

any aberrant contraction of the leg muscles which will result in your knees rotating in, locking or bracing backwards. A word of caution here: you do not want to create tension in your knee joints through inducing muscular collapse by actively or deliberately bending them.

The feet

As we have already noted Alexander found out that the instruction given to him by his acting coach to 'take hold of the floor with your feet' resulted in his toes being contracted and bent downwards which produced an undue arching of the feet. Many of us will be able to identify with that misuse. For that reason we need to keep in mind that we do not possess the flat, extremely elastic and prehensile feet of other primates that are so useful in tree climbing. In fact one very important function of your parallel aligned toes is for balancing and feeling the ground. You can explore this by standing on one foot and then flexing your toes upwards so that none of them are in contact with the floor. It's difficult to maintain balance, isn't it? Your toes also play a vitally important role in locomotion. So you can also experiment with walking forward or backward with similarly upwardly-flexed toes on both feet. That will result in a tightening of your leg joints and torso and a pattern of movement which is very stiff and awkward.

Be aware also that ill-fitting shoes impair balance and movement. If footwear is too tight then your feet are mechanically compressed, but if too loose – flip-flops, for example – your toes will grip to try and prevent them falling off. By using inappropriate footwear you are adding to your repertoire of misuse. We return to this in Chapter 5.

So what is the best way to think of your feet in contact with the ground? Assuming that you have inhibited and given the directions for the primary control, you will now want to establish an open contact with the floor. Most of us stand with too much weight on the front of the feet. If that is the case with you, then a way needs to be found of coming back from the pivot point of your ankle joints in such a way that the three contact points of the feet – the areas around your large, robust heels, big toes and little toes – are equalised. But this is not just a matter of thinking of your feet in isolation; instead, it is a function of your general coordination. In essence, balance on two feet is achieved not by 'doing' but by giving directions for the primary control and then adding on suitable orders for your ankles, knees and hip joints so that all of your body's joint surfaces are opening out away from each other and your feet are releasing into the ground. We cover this in Chapter 4.

The shoulders and arms

We will look at the way the shoulders, arms and hands work and relevant directions in Chapters 4 and 8. It's sufficient to note at this point that because the shoulder girdle is so flexible and mobile, it is very easy to end up doing a variety of inappropriate things. For example, you can pull your shoulder blades up towards the base of the neck and head, or pull them back and down, or pull them together, rather than allowing them to lie flat and widened on the back of your expanded rib cage as they should.

Considering how easy it is to make unnecessary tension in the arms, it is also worth bearing in mind that if you are standing and not doing anything, your limbs, in conjunction with your lengthening and widening back, can hang freely by the sides, with the backs of your hands facing slightly forwards and the thumbs directed to lengthen. In turn, the weight of your outward releasing arms will encourage the whole of your shoulder girdle to release into width. You can further amplify that effect by directing your shoulders to release away from each other.

The sequence of directions

The directions – conscious 'mental' orders – are to be given, according to Alexander, 'altogether, one after the other'. So the great challenge for students of the technique is to learn how to transform normal linear thinking into holistic three-dimensional directing. Properly achieved that will achieve a balanced pattern of working between extensor and flexor muscles of the body appropriate to whatever activity you happen to be involved in, whether it is talking to friends, watching TV, or peeling a pineapple.

Giving directions might all sound quite mysterious and even though it will be unfamiliar to most people, the steps involved are quite straightforward. To get the orders to work properly, however, you need to be conscious of the sequence, and then memorise it. But I want to emphasise once again that the process of achieving a better working of the primary control begins by looking out and becoming aware of your environment without any commitment to perform an action. In other words you want your eyes to work properly and see something *before* you start directing or moving.

It's also vitally important that looking out to see something should not only precede but also *continue* throughout the process of directing. If you become aware that you are blanking off you need to come back to the present by reminding yourself to look out. Also if you find that in attempting to direct your eyes are moving around – for example, going up or down when you think of the spine lengthening or ankles releasing, or side to side when you think of the shoulders widening away from each other – it signals that you are actively trying to feel it out and trying to be 'right' rather than simply thinking the orders. Check that tendency otherwise the likelihood is that you will be trapped in sensation monitoring which will interfere with your ability to learn how to direct correctly.

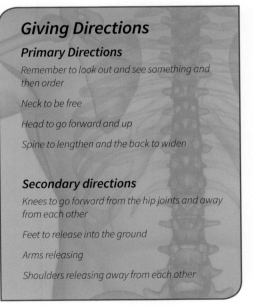

Giving Directions

Primary Directions

Remember to look out and see something and then order

Neck to be free

Head to go forward and up

Spine to lengthen and the back to widen

Secondary directions

Knees to go forward from the hip joints and away from each other

Feet to release into the ground

Arms releasing

Shoulders releasing away from each other

The second phase is to add on a direction to free your neck, followed by your head, and then your back, so that all the directions for the primary control are running at the same time. Put another way, if each direction is a spinning plate, then all three plates are spinning simultaneously at the end of the process. You can then add on a direction for your knees to release forward and away from each other. The result will be that your body releases in multiple directions creating a toned elastic stretch in the musculature. This is what Alexander called 'antagonistic actions' or 'antagonistic pulls'. The way you are taught to activate them in the technique is unique.

Above Arsenal and England forward Theo Walcott (left) demonstrating great coordination in movement

Finally, depending on what you are doing – reading a newspaper, using a computer keyboard, using a mobile phone, playing a violin, kicking a football or talking to a friend – there might well be additional plates that need to be spun for specific ways of using the arms and hands. And the trick is to keep the required number of plates spinning for as long as you can.

Directions as words

Of course initially the directions as words will only be meaningful through the experience of a teacher's hands, or, as Alexander discovered, through observation in the mirrors (and for us through digital imaging to some extent). When Alexander was looking at his reflection he would have been thinking about what he was seeing but he would not have needed to use words to interpret his experience. It was through communicating with others, initially through speech and later through writing pamphlets and books, what was involved in the interlinked processes of inhibition and direction, that he was obliged to translate a visual and kinaesthetic experience.

As we have already noted there is an inherent ambiguity in words, which is more or less problematic depending on what sort of problem you are trying to solve. For example, it is one thing following the instructions for assembling a piece of flat-packed furniture and something else when it comes to trying to convey a complex multi-dimensional body-self experience into what are, by comparison, one-dimensional representations. Take, for instance, the direction 'let the head go forward and up'. That phrase will mean a range of things to people untutored in the Alexander Technique. Because of the everyday association of the head with the face in Western culture, the likelihood is that most people without experience of the technique will interpret that to mean that they should 'do' something, such as actively tilt the face upwards, thus pulling the head back and down, which is the exact opposite of what is intended.

Words have significant limitations, then, in conveying what's involved in the technique. Really it is the mental directions that count. But what exactly is directing? Well, you know by now that even though it generates an optimum lengthening of the muscles it is not a form of 'doing'. You also know that unless you are exceptionally well-coordinated you cannot rely on your kinaesthetic or proprioceptive sense. So directing involves changing messages which normally go from the subconscious parts of the brain into the body's mechanisms to a conscious level without either trying to 'do' anything, or by deliberately trying to create a feeling or sensation.

In order to get this message across Alexander would sometimes compare what is involved in directing to the type of cognition involved in making a wish. In a lecture to a group of physical education students in 1934 he put it this way: 'But if we are going to do, not mechanical exercise, but something real that matters, you have to think beforehand the means whereby you have to do it, and give the directions or orders for these means whereby, in the form of a wish, as it were, and keep that wish going all through the activity.'

This leads to a further issue. Many people might think it is impossible to direct without using words. But reflection reveals that we employ that mental capacity all the time in the course of our everyday routines. No words are required when you think of a geometric shape, remember a sunset, or recall a piece of music. So when, for example, you are having an Alexander lesson being guided by my hands, or standing by yourself in front of the mirror and giving your directions for the head, neck, back and limbs there is no need to use words – other than perhaps as a convenient way to remember the sequence of directing.

Overall the choice of words used in the Alexander Technique is not so important as long as they refer back to an objective psycho-physical reality – that is, yourself. That said, some words may be better than others for some of us. Instead, for example, of thinking of the spine (or back) lengthening and widening, many students find it preferable to think 'torso to lengthen and widen' as for them the phrase seems to capture something of our three-dimensional reality in a way that 'back to lengthen and widen' does not.

Additionally, in order to avoid boredom and mere verbal repetition – giving orders as a type of meaningless formula or mantra – you might also find it useful to sometimes invert the directions for the primary control and the secondary directions in order to more clearly understand the nature of the problem that is to be solved, namely, the un-doing of habitual and unnecessary tension in your body. So:

- Don't blank off or fix the eyes

- Don't stiffen the neck

- Don't pull the head back and down (or forward and down)

- Don't shorten the spine and narrow the back (or torso)

- Don't stiffen the hip joints and pull the knees together (or deliberately bend them)

- Don't scrunch up the feet

- Don't stiffen the arms and hands

In the final analysis, then, the words are merely verbal hooks on which the directions, metaphorically defined as wishes, are hung. So although I use a form of words that make sense to me, if I think that you do not understand what I'm saying I will either change the form of words, or try to show you what I mean in the mirror in order to cut through the problems of translation.

You will also want to keep in mind that the visual and kinaesthetic experiences produced by lessons in the Alexander Technique are key to learning, otherwise there is a danger that being overly concerned about the precise meaning of words – what is a neck? what is a knee? what is a shoulder? – might lead to an infinite regress. But once you have made progress you should feel free to develop your own vocabulary for the directions based both on what you have learnt in lessons as well as observation of your own image in the mirror. You might be interested to know that one of my students has simplified the directions to 'Up, down and widen'. That might not work for everybody, but it certainly works for her. One of my favourite set of directions, however, comes from Alexander himself. He once said to a student: 'Give your orders, head forward and up, down with the shoulders, widen the back, and make no trouble about it; one thing does the other'. Brilliant!

The role of movement

Although conscious inhibition and directing are the foundation of the Alexander Technique, nothing much would happen without movement. Inhibition and the directions create pathways from the brain and central nervous system into the musculature, but significant physical changes are only really brought about when movement takes place. As Alexander discovered his ability to maintain the orders was compromised as soon as he began to speak – a type of movement – which triggered his habitual pattern of vocalisation. The way to solve the problem of habit is to be able to inhibit, direct and crucially to maintain the directions throughout any movement in which you happen to be engaged.

Thinking in activity

Although the theory behind the Alexander Technique is simple enough I have yet to encounter anyone who finds the practice of thinking in activity easy – at least initially. There are two reasons for this. First, we all have a strong preference to perform actions that are familiar at a sensory level – move the head, move a limb, or perform an exercise of one sort or another, rather than engage with something that feels kinaesthetically unfamiliar or odd, or which for some of us may not at first *appear* to provide *any* sensory feedback even though objective changes are taking place. The second is that the human mind has evolved to handle and remember social information (gossip or chit-chat about family, friends and so on) far more easily than any type of technical-factual stuff, including that relevant to the operation and direction of our own bodies. But the starting point for the Alexander Technique involves conscious inhibition, the ability not to respond to a stimulus in a habitual way, together with multiple overlapping directions followed either by moving or not moving. Nonetheless Alexander thinking, which precedes and then informs and guides movement and other aspects of the body-mind complex, is a skill that most people can learn if they want to. Over time inhibition and giving the directions take place simultaneously as a seamless flow.

Examples of thinking in activity in our everyday lives

Here are three everyday examples of Alexander thinking in activity with which we are all familiar.

Carrying a shopping bag

You have been shopping. You are now going to pick up the shopping bag, which might weigh several kilos or more, from the counter or floor. Obviously carrying a loaded bag creates a demand on your system. But the relevant question is: are you carrying the weight efficiently or not? The truth is that most of us are not. Instead of allowing the weight of the bag to go through the body into the ground, most of us hold the weight in the arm, neck and shoulders thus causing unnecessary tension not only locally but throughout the body. So even allowing for structural problems, which will vary between individuals, much of this unnecessary tension is being directly triggered by the wrong sort of messages generated in the central nervous system that flow into the musculature.

Above Carrying loads on the head is customary in many non-Western cultures

It's revealing that in Africa, the Indian subcontinent, Latin America, and elsewhere, loads are often routinely carried on the head. If a young person has learned the technique well from their elders and is well-practised, the evidence suggests that head porterage is a very efficient method of transportation. That's not customary behaviour in Anglo-American influenced cultures. So what's the best way for you to carry a shopping bag? A key point is to avoid creating unnecessary tension at any point in either the lifting or carrying process. It helps greatly if your primary control is working reasonably well. Then you can inhibit and direct your hand to open without creating undue tension in the wrist and insert extended or lengthening fingers into the handle in such a way that your hand forms a 'hook' grip. Your thumb should be directed to remain lengthened and passive. Now take the weight without stiffening your arm or shoulders. You also need to avoid leaning to one side and displacing your pelvis, which will interfere with the workings of your legs and feet.

It's also very important to remember not to keep picking up the weight of the bag as you walk along – instead, allow it to lengthen your arm without locking or stiffening your elbow. Note also that your hand will face slightly forward if your back is widening. If the activity is performed well the only real work being done is the fingers creating a hook. Then the weight of the shopping bag passes up the bones of your arm, across your shoulder girdle, and down along the length of your contra-rotating spine, and through the long bones of the legs, through your feet, and into the ground.

What happens, though, if you are walking along and you realise you are making a mess of things – you are leaning to one side, pulling your shoulders up, pulling your back in, or your arm muscles are beginning to experience fatigue? There are a number of options. Obviously you can try to endure it. You can also try to ignore it and blot out the discomfort or pain by distracting yourself in some way. Alternatively, you can stay in the moment and use what you have learned through the Alexander Technique. That gives you two additional options. First, inhibit your immediate impulse to put things 'right', then give the directive orders outlined above to counteract at least some of the misuse that is occurring as you continue to walk along. That will almost certainly help. However it may not get to the root of the problem since it takes a lot of Alexander experience to be able to transform bad coordination into good coordination whilst in movement. So the second option is to stop, put the bag on the floor, come to upright and then proceed to inhibit and give the directions to get an improved working of your primary control and your limbs before picking up the bag again – this time without causing unnecessary tension.

Picking up keys from the floor

You are standing in the hallway about to leave your home, with keys in hand, which you then accidentally drop on the floor. Most people's reaction will be to reach down and pick them up in a way that is habitual, but which will not be biomechanically efficient.

The 'keys on the floor must pick them up' scenario will generate different responses amongst different people – some through a combination of genetics and upbringing are 'slow' reactors, some 'fast'. It will also depend on the situation. For example, it is probable that the importance of retrieving the keys from the floor will be judged less urgent if you are on holiday, or if it is the weekend and you are not in any great rush to leave the house. But if you are late for an important meeting at work, or due to meet a friend and you are aware that the clock is ticking, the chances are that the impulse to pick up the keys quickly will be much greater than when there's no time pressure.

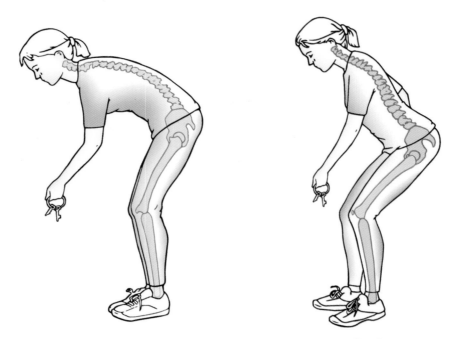

Above There are worse and better ways of picking objects off the floor

Your response will also likely vary according to your relative position in the social order. If you are the boss, for example, it may well be that you will experience less pressure than if you are an employee. You will also take into account your perception of other people's expectations of your behaviour ('don't worry, he's always on time' or 'don't worry, he's always late'). Culture is important too. Most traditional and developing societies have a much more relaxed or elastic notion of 'time' and 'efficiency' than those that are deeply embedded in market economies where 'time is of the essence' or 'time is money'.

So identical 'physical' situations where keys need to be picked up from the floor will have different levels of meaning or significance, depending on the situation you find yourself in. Yet whatever the social and cultural context, the central point from an Alexander Technique perspective is to consider inhibiting your immediate response to the stimulus 'keys on floor pick them up'.

There are many different ways to efficiently pick something off the floor, of course. In all cases, before lowering your height you should look out, inhibit and give your directions for the primary control so that you achieve better balance on two feet. One way to bend is to assume a reasonably wide base with your toes well turned out and maintaining the directions to your neck, head, back, add on directions for the legs and feet, allow yourself to move down in space to a point where you can retrieve the keys without tightening and losing internal length. On the return journey maintain the relationship between your neck, head and back, put your knees away from each other while directing the ankles together and slowly return to upright without shortening or narrowing your torso, or tightening your legs and feet.

The meeting

So there you are listening to a presentation by a boss, colleague or visitor. As time goes by and mental-physical fatigue (and possibly boredom) have set in, you are no longer sitting upright, supported by the back of the chair, with your feet on the ground, but have slumped into a C-shaped curve, with at least some of your upper body weight propped up by leaning on one or other elbow and your legs crossed at the ankles and tucked underneath you.

But something the speaker has said has caught your interest. You now wish to make a point to the presenter and the rest of the group. Before saying your piece and in order to appear engaged, you decide to sit up 'straight' as befits the rules of modern corporate culture in which slouching and speaking at the same time, especially to a social superior or a guest speaker, is disapproved of.

The problem is that by sitting up 'straight' the slump you were in has not disappeared. Instead you have just pulled it in a different direction. In fact you are still losing internal length, but have added a good dose of stiffening in order to appear 'present' and 'attentive'. Furthermore, in your speedy attempt to 'sit up straight' you are activating your body's white muscle fibres, which respond quickly, but tire rapidly ending up in another spinal collapse.

When you also consider that any form of slump or sit up 'straight' stiffening will affect your ability to breathe, the tone of your vocal delivery and your ability to organise your thoughts, it is in your interest to think of another method of getting your point across. How you accomplish this in a meeting is very similar to the methods used in the previous examples. It's best to pause, look out and give your orders for the primary control. Then place both feet on the floor, your lower legs vertical. Now allow your upper body to rotate forward or backward slowly a fraction at a time from your hip joints, without pulling the legs together or pushing them apart, in such a way that your spine releases into length and your back widens. Pause and then come back to the vertical maintaining the poise of your head releasing away from your downward-pointing sitting bones. Alternatively you can use your hands to lift yourself up and move yourself either to the back or front of the chair allowing yourself to come to upright as you move.

Above A typical office meeting. Note in particular how a combination of feet crossed and tucked under accentuates a C-shaped or hunched curvature of the spine, pulling the head down on to the neck

It's also worth bearing in mind that if you wish to demonstrate empathy to the speaker or other members of the group by leaning in make sure that once you are sitting upright you rotate forward from your hip joints and not somewhere in the middle or top of the spine, as that will result in pulling back your head. Now, maintaining your orders to the head, neck and back you are ready to make your point. Or not.

The role of inhibition and directing in everyday life

As the everyday examples of carrying a bag, picking up keys from the floor, and contributing to a meeting demonstrate, the overall aim of the Alexander Technique is to encourage you to think in activity – any activity – and generate a more efficient working of the head, neck and back relationship, which will result in a lengthening of the stature. It's what Alexander teachers more colloquially call 'going up' – rather than a shortening of the stature –'pulling down'.

Using inhibition and giving appropriate directions allows us to suspend, to a greater or lesser extent, our habitual response to a stimulus and perform an activity in a different and more coordinated way. Over time, repetition of conscious inhibition and direction generates improved general and specific patterns of coordination in an increasing number of activities, including standing, the subject of the next chapter.

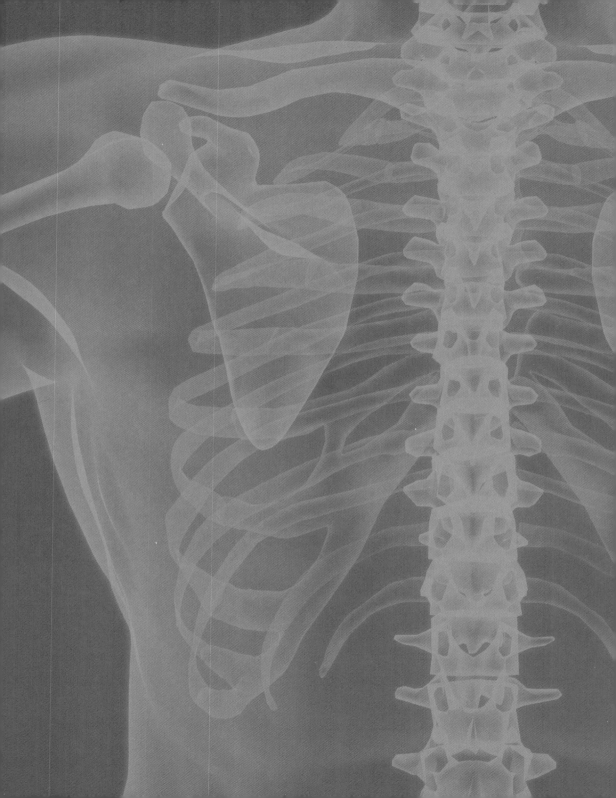

Chapter 4 – *Standing*

'After his first gasp of breath at birth perhaps the greatest physical achievement in any human being's life is the moment when he has mastered balance and breathing sufficiently to stand steady on his own two feet'

Raymond Dart

'The human foot is a masterpiece of engineering and a work of art'

Leonardo da Vinci

Standing upright

Standing upright, the head poised on top of the spine, is a truly remarkable achievement. Many biological anthropologists believe it is the key defining feature of *Homo sapiens* since only the human primate is able to come to a fully upright stance with fully extended knee and hip joints in such a way that the thigh bones align with the bones of the lower leg to form flexible, continuous vertical columns. With our joints stabilised by ligaments, body weight is then efficiently transmitted through the spine, pelvis, legs and the platforms of the feet into the ground, notably without much need to use the body's large, powerful muscles such as the gluteals, quadriceps and calves.

The result is that when in dynamic balance, swaying slightly, we have the capacity to remain standing for a significant amount of time. Other mammals can stand on their hind legs without using their forelimbs for support – primates such as bonobos, chimpanzees and baboons, and also bears and meerkats – though they only manage to do so for relatively short periods because of the high energy cost used in counteracting the pull of gravity on their unstable, semi-flexed bodies. Nevertheless, the limited ability by some animals to stand on two legs provides an important clue about the type of habitual erect bipedalism that is unique to our species. The development of a more vertically-oriented spine amongst early hominins several million years ago likely evolved through the benefits accrued through their standing on branches or on the ground with a full-foot contact and on the tips of their toes (as well as squatting) to reach fruit and other foods. True bipedal walking or running only emerged later. In short, our ape-like ancestors stood upright before they moved upright.

Gravity and the extensor and flexor muscles

In a quadruped chimpanzee the centre of gravity lies in the midsection of the torso, between the arms and legs, whereas in the human biped it is to be found backwards and upwards, just a little way above the bottom two bones of the spinal column. In a well-balanced human the line of gravity passes through the ear down through a point which lies approximately halfway between the lumbar vertebrae at the rear and the belly button at the front of the torso, continuing past the front of the knee and through the feet. From a side perspective, the shoulders, hip joints and

Above The centre of gravity in a quadruped chimpanzee is located differently to that of a well-balanced standing human

ankles will be aligned. The result is that there is more weight in front of the spine than behind it, and so an upright human has a tendency to fall forwards – clearly demonstrated, for example, whenever someone faints.

The role of the extensor muscles, also known as the anti-gravity muscles, which run mostly down the back of the neck and torso, and combine with those in the legs, is to dynamically maintain this unstable uprightness by creating an elastic stretch between the occiput, the bony bit at the rear of the skull, which should be releasing forward and up, and the feet, especially the heels, which are releasing back and down into the ground towards the centre of the Earth. In standing the flexor muscles at the front of your body which are employed in bending, grasping and lifting, should be relatively passive. A practical way to engage with this is to think of the front of your trunk as simply the front of your supportive back musculature.

The ills of uprightness

Unlike many other animals, such as cats, dogs, horses and deer, which stand either on the balls of their feet or on the tips of their toes, the human biped has evolved to make a full-foot contact with the ground. Although it is certainly possible for us to stand for hours using only seven per cent more energy than while lying on the ground, the sheer volume of problems associated with uprightness – including flat feet, heel spurs, Achilles tendinitis, osteoarthritis in the leg joints, varicose veins, sway back (lordosis), a sideways curvature of the spine (scoliosis), a rounded upper back or hunch back (kyphosis), spontaneously fractured vertebrae, and herniated intervertebral discs – has led many scientists to claim that we are the victims of a poor evolutionary outcome. 'The human vertebral column is unique in its sinusoidal curvatures that allow the upper body to balance over the hips,' says anatomist and biological anthropologist Bruce Latimer. 'Turning a spine originally adapted for a quadruped into one that is perpendicular to the ground has resulted in numerous problems that are unique to our species. If you take care of it, your spine will get you through to about 40 or 50. After that you are on your own.'

Other scientists, however, dismiss the idea that maladaptation in bipedalism is responsible for the so-called ills of uprightness such as back pain. 'If that were true, natural selection would have its toll and we'd be extinct,' argues evolutionary biologist Daniel Lieberman. 'What is more likely is that many people sit in chairs all day, get no exercise, and thus have weak backs. We did not evolve to sit in chairs all day.'

Research conducted by medical scientist David Garlick supports this perspective. Nearly everyone examined in his Laboratory for Musculoskeletal and Postural Research at the

University of New South Wales suffered to a greater or lesser extent from poor balance and coordination because of inappropriate use of muscles against gravity in standing –'head thrust forward with an over-curved neck, sloping or hunched shoulders, humped back, over-arched or flattened lumbar curve, protruding abdomen, hyper-extended knees'. That's an impressive list!

The study also revealed that in malcoordinated subjects the abdominal and chest muscles were stiffened or over-contracted to help stabilise or support the torso, while, by contrast, others, especially the back muscles, were underused or under-contracted and showed obvious signs of atrophy. This imbalance between the body's extensor and flexor muscles was also found to affect breathing. People with poor tone in the back muscles had less abdominal movement in respiration, taking more and shallower breaths than another group of subjects who had undergone training in the Alexander Technique.

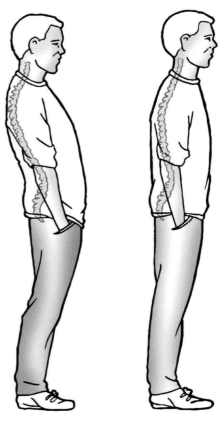

Above On the left a typical upright slouch, while on the right achieving a better balance

Leaving aside congenital causes or the effects of conditions, such as polio on the body's musculature, from a diagnostic point of view Dr Garlick recommended that his medical colleagues ought to view many of the problems associated with uprightness as preventable repetitive strain injuries. 'It is perfectly possible to use muscle at the low levels necessary to maintain the upright position, sitting and standing, without a sense of fatigue,' he explained. 'Joints and other non-muscular tissues may give rise to discomfort if a person sits or stands motionless but red muscle fibres themselves will not fatigue.'

So the important question is: if you do have to stand for any period, how do you accomplish it efficiently and effectively?

Standing with 'good posture'

When people who know something of the Alexander Technique but have no direct experience of it find out that they are talking to an Alexander teacher (normally by getting an answer to the question, 'What do you do for a living?'), they will invariably try to improve their 'posture' by trying to stand (or sit) up 'straight'. Unfortunately, that's the wrong way to go about improving one's general coordination and relationship with gravity. In Western culture the meaning of standing up 'straight' – so-called good posture – has been hugely influenced by military-type bearing as well as deportment etiquette. Debrett's, the organisation dedicated to the preservation of British 'aristocratic' values, summarises that tradition very well: 'Hold your head high, keep your back straight and pull your shoulders back.'

If you are a habitual collapser, who tries to improve static 'posture' by standing up 'straight', be aware that you are creating a host of new problems. There are at least five reasons why. Firstly, standing tall by holding the head 'high' is just another way of pulling your head back and down on to your neck. Secondly, by interfering with your head balance you are now lifting your chest, which in turn results in pushing your hip joints forward, creating an excessive curvature of the lumbar spine. Thirdly, the effort you are using in lifting your chest is having an unfortunate effect of tightening and narrowing the space between your shoulder blades. Fourthly, to prevent any loss of balance you have to stiffen your legs at the ankles, knees and hip joints. Finally, by trying to stand up straight you are over-activating the white or fast-switch muscle fibres in your body and that's the reason you are now feeling tense or tired.

It's somewhat of a paradox then, that if you try to achieve better posture by pulling 'up', you actually achieve the opposite and pull 'down'. Debrett's and other institutions such as the army and many dance academies, where 'good posture' is a badge of membership, have a lot to answer for.

Above Balancing a book on the head is a traditional deportment exercise

Balancing on the ground

Some psychotherapists talk to their clients about the importance of achieving emotional (and sometimes spiritual) grounding in order to initiate a change in orientation towards oneself, other people and the 'physical' world. The instruction typically offered is to 'feel' that the ground is solid beneath one's feet. Although the problem of people not experiencing a connection to the ground is real, on its own this does not really tackle the fundamental problem of poor balance and faulty kinaesthesia.

In reality it is impossible to be 'emotionally' grounded unless one is also 'physically' grounded. Moreover from a functional perspective it does not make sense to split the self into different components – emotional, intellectual, spiritual, and so on – and imagine that there are different things to do for different parts of oneself. It's far better to accept that you operate as a unity and try to achieve or maintain a better balance when carrying out any activity, whether you are standing at a bus stop or waiting your turn to perform the high jump. The important point to understand is that a genuine experience of 'grounding' cannot be achieved directly. Indeed becoming grounded and going up to your full height is one and the same thing. The danger is that if you separate it out you either collapse or try to pull yourself 'up'. On the other hand, if the two polarities –'up' and 'down' – are understood as something that work together as an anti-gravity response in your body you will get a more favourable outcome.

Coordination in standing

In his first book *Man's Supreme Inheritance*, Alexander rightly pointed out that there can be no such thing as a correct standing position for each and every person, for the simple reason that everyone is built differently. The problem to solve, then, is not one of finding a correct position, but working towards improved coordination and balance for any particular individual. Nevertheless, Alexander makes some excellent general points about standing. They are certainly worth bearing in mind whenever you are on two feet, either at work or at leisure.

As an actor Alexander would have been very familiar with standing with one foot a few inches in front of the other, with the heel of the front foot more or less opposite the ankle of the rear one, since it helps to create conditions for stability as well as movement. This 'open' attitude is often used today by television news presenters, some classically-trained singers and in a more exaggerated form by soccer players about to take a free or corner kick.

Alexander suggested that the weight of the body should rest chiefly on the rear foot. But it is obvious that that cannot happen if the pelvic girdle is displaced too far forward, a pattern of holding that many of us do. Do not be tempted, however, to 'level' the pelvis by tightening the abdominal, gluteal or other muscles to 'engage your core' or 'tuck your tailbone under'. If you do this you will only create additional tension – yet another 'different form of badly'– rather than a genuine release of your body's musculature that will bring you up to your full height.

Instead, you need to inhibit and direct and then allow your pelvis and hip joints to release up and back far enough to allow the weight of your upper body to be transferred to the rear foot without actively leaning forward. At the same time your knees should be directed forwards and away from each other. As well as engaging your supportive back musculature standing in this way has an additional advantage. It will allow you to transfer weight between your front and back foot, which helps to prevent fixation and rigidity, especially in the muscles of the ankle joints which play a key role in proprioception. Furthermore it leaves open the possibility of moving forward, backward or sideways.

Above Ivory Coast forward Didier Drogba prepares to take a free kick by placing one foot behind the other

When placing your feet you can experiment with putting one foot in front of or behind the other. You will tend to find that the latter is easier to perform as our misuse in moving backward is much less pronounced than when going forward. But try not to make a fetish out of this procedure. It's worth noting that over time Alexander relied less and less on this kind of instruction, and placed far more emphasis on on-going balanced coordination. If your primary control is working well and you have developed a reasonably accurate kinaesthetic sense, more or less everything else falls into place.

The role of the shoulders in balanced standing

If you have an on-going habit of distorting the shoulder girdle – for example, by holding them forward and up as an accompaniment to slouching while sitting, throwing them forward when you go from sit to stand, or tightening in some way as a response to stress and anxiety – then this pattern needs to be addressed otherwise it will interfere with your balance in standing and other activities.

In the early years of his teaching, Alexander invited students who were raising their shoulders, in conjunction with directions for the primary control, to order them to release 'back and down'. However, after discovering that this order encouraged most people to do something rather than simply give a mental direction he then opted to provide the relevant kinaesthetic experience without accompanying words. He decided the less said the better. Here is another way to solve this particularly tricky conundrum. Stand with your feet together or fore-aft underneath your head. Give the directions for the primary control and think of an upward release through your ankles, knees and hips. Order your fingers and thumbs to lengthen before gently opening your hands so that your fingers point towards the floor. Now add on another direction for your shoulders to release and widen – remember it is a thought so do not be tempted to pull your shoulders back – and allow me to turn one of your hands around the axis of a lengthening little finger so that your palm is facing forward. I will then repeat the process for your other limb. Be aware that to achieve a balance between widening the front and back of your upper torso it is important that you do not pull the inside edge of your shoulder blades towards one another.

When both hands are in place, your elbows close to your trunk and fingers lengthening, I will ask you to direct your shoulder blades to release into your back at the same time as your pelvis and tailbone are ordered to drop back and down towards your ankles or heels, all the while maintaining the upward direction along the spine, your head also releasing forward and up.

The next step is to allow me to rotate your lengthening thumb so that the back of one hand is facing forward once more. At this point you need to inhibit any tendency for the spiral movement generated in your lower arm to travel beyond the elbow joint. In that way you will maintain the connection of the upper part of your arm back and down into your back. If all has gone well you will now be standing on two feet in better balance. Take advantage of your improved connection with the ground to release up and back a fraction from your ankle joints. You are now ready to explore how balance in your shoulder girdle is also important for going on to the toes.

Going up on to the toes

Jessica Ennis-Hill

Whenever British heptathlete Jessica Ennis-Hill prepares for the run up in the high jump she walks forward a couple of paces, stops and stands with her feet underneath her head, about three inches apart. She pauses and then without losing height goes vertically up on to her toes.

She stays there for a couple of seconds and while remaining on tiptoe places her left foot a few inches in front of her. Now she quickly releases back to the ground, lowers her height by bending at her ankles, knees and hip joints, puts one leg behind the other, leans back whilst keeping her internal length and begins her run up by releasing up and forward from the pivot points of her ankles. The London Olympics 2012 heptathlon champion delivers a masterclass in how to maintain balance and generate an increase in muscular springiness by balancing on the toes in preparation for moving forward and jumping over a very high object.

Whichever way Ennis-Hill has come to the procedure of going on to the toes – whether it is something she was taught, or whether it is something she has developed by herself – it clearly works in giving her a sense of upward direction and release before she accelerates forwards to fly through the air. The Sheffield-born athlete stands at 1.65 metres (5'5") and, despite a relatively small stature, is the joint British record holder for the outdoor event at 1.95 metres (6' 5"). Interestingly, apart from the high jump and long jump, Ennis-Hill does not perform going on to her toes in any of the other disciplines of the heptathlon. Perhaps she should.

Going up on to the toes

Going up on to flexible toes using the strong, stable arches of our feet has played an important part in the evolution of the

Above Jessica Ennis-Hill poised on tip-toe before beginning her high jump run-up

uprightness and mobility of our species. Indeed at some point in our lives, usually in childhood, most of us will have achieved balanced bipedal standing. For various reasons later in life you might have lost the ability to stand upright efficiently. It obviously makes sense to try to restore it so that you can stand and move around the world once again with ease. One way is to learn how to consciously and efficiently go up on to your toes.

Although providing less stability than standing with a full foot contact, the movement on to the toes facilitates a significant lengthening of the stature through elevated mechanical activity in the extensor musculature of your neck, back, hips, knees and ankles. It also tones the muscles of your feet and, except in the most extreme cases where your genes have produced fallen arches, makes the need for orthotics redundant. Alexander routinely taught going up on to the toes to his pupils in their later lessons. It's important not only in itself, but also because it forms the basis of reaching for objects that are above standing height, as well as providing the necessary information, should you need it, about using high heels without damaging the feet and ankles.

In performing going up on to the toes it is very important that you do not pull your head back, lift your chest and arch your back. You may *feel* that doing it in this way helps you to achieve more height, but the reality is that this over-activity of your musculature will result in compression. You will still be able to go on to your toes, but it will be at the expense of good coordination and balance.

To prevent this I will perform some preliminary work to improve the working of your primary control, while you place your feet a little way apart with the toes pointing out slightly. I will then stand behind you with my hands around the lower part of your chest, my thumbs at the rear and my fingers spreading around the sides of your rib cage. Alternatively, I will place the flat of my hands on your shoulder blades. You should inhibit any direct attempt to go on to your toes throughout the procedure. You also need to know that I am not going to lift you.

Now resist the gentle but increasing forward direction coming from my hands by coming backward as a unit from your ankle joints while keeping all the directions going. The important thing as you move back in space is to maintain an upward release through your ankles, knees and hips. It's also crucial that you leave your toes lengthening, rather than pushing them down against the floor.

If you are able to maintain a reasonable degree of inhibition and directing as you come back to my hands, you will go up on to the balls of your feet and then on to your toes smoothly and efficiently, without even trying. If that does not happen it means that you have interfered in some way. Many students try to 'help' in a variety of ways by pushing the pelvis backwards or forwards, or pushing the ankles outwards. The result is a loss of height.

But assuming the activity has gone well and you are now up on the toes, then, after a few seconds I will ask you to release your ankles while maintaining your internal length by thinking of the back or crown of your head and heels going in opposite directions, and slowly return to the ground.

The activity can be repeated several times. Going up on to your toes, as with all Alexander activities, will tend to become better organised and coordinated when performed on the second or third attempt as the release becomes embedded in your neuromuscular system.

Going up on to the toes on your own

Once you have performed going on to the toes a few times in a lesson, it is then possible to practice the activity on your own. Always remember, however, that the Alexander Technique is not about mechanical exercise, but is concerned with thinking in activity, through inhibition and direction. With this in mind, place a high-backed chair in front of you with your feet a little way apart and turned out slightly. Then refuse to do anything at all. Give your orders and then place your fingertips, either palms down or up, or the knuckles of both hands on the top rail of the chair.

You have already learnt in a lesson that it is important not to pull your head back and bring your body forward but to release up and back to go up on to the toes. It might seem impossible to achieve this as you stand with your feet on the ground, but this is where you have to trust in the directions and hope that they work. (If they do not then you need to take a different approach by stopping and thinking through the sequence.) A good idea is to think of coming up and back from your ankles *before* you attempt to go on to the balls of your feet and then on to the toes. Also remember that there is no rush, and it is perfectly all right to stand with your fingertips touching the chair, inhibiting and giving directions for five or 10 minutes, or even longer. Of course, whatever the time taken you then have the option of going through with the activity, doing nothing at all, or doing something different such as walking backward.

If you have decided to carry out the activity and you are now on your toes, come back to the floor in the same way as you have learnt in a lesson. Maintain the lengthening of stature, and then allow your ankles to release so that you are once more on the ground. If you are successful you can try going on to your toes without the support of the chair. You can perform it not only in your home, but in the office or while waiting for a bus or train.

If you want a more dynamic stretch, especially along the hamstrings, you can place a couple of thin paperback books on the floor a few inches apart, with the spines facing away from you. Now inhibit, direct and walk forward so that the balls of your feet are on the paperbacks with the heels on the ground. Go on to your toes and return to the floor as previously described.

Using the wall

Throughout his teaching career Alexander kept on trying to find new ways to counter the near universal tendency in throwing the body forward and pulling the head down on to the neck. Using a wall or door for support in movement, including going up on to the toes, was devised to make it easier for students to achieve better coordination and especially to obtain release in the lower back and hip joints. I find that wall work is particularly useful for some new students, especially when the mechanisms of balance in the body are changing. I will introduce it to you when it is appropriate. Later on you can perform it by yourself. Bear in mind when carrying out the procedure on your own that it is best to use a wall or door with a smooth surface in order to minimise any friction. If you can, use mirrors to monitor what is going on.

Going down the wall

Stand around three or four inches away from the wall, with your feet a little way apart and the toes turned out slightly. Remember to keep your field of attention as large as possible, so look out and see what is around you. Give yourself the stimulus to come back to the wall as a unit keeping your extended toes on the ground. Then inhibit and direct, and, at the moment of your choice, allow yourself to release up and back from your free ankle joints. Remember not to fix your rib cage as you sway backwards as you do not want to interfere with the breathing.

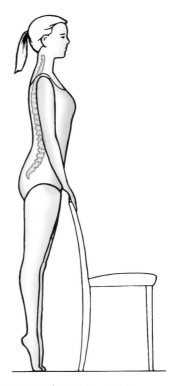

Above Going on to the toes on your own

Going on to the toes

Look out

Inhibit and direct

Stand in front of a chair with your toes turned out slightly

Place your fingertips on the top rail of the chair for support

Think of coming up and back from your ankles, before going on to the balls of the feet, and then on to the toes

Maintain your internal length as you allow your ankle joints to release so that you come back to the ground

It's very important that both your shoulder blades and the lower lumbar spine and pelvic girdle contact the wall at the same time. If, however, you are habitually twisted, you will tend to find that one side will contact the wall first. Also, if you have a habit of displacing your pelvis forward and arching the lower back, the likelihood is that your shoulders will touch the wall, but not your pelvis. You might also find that the back of your head is touching the wall. In a lesson I will make suitable adjustments to prevent any or all of these things happening, which you will need to keep in mind when carrying out the procedure on your own.

Once you have a good contact with the wall, inhibit and give your directions for the primary control. Then add on a direction for an upward release through your ankles, knees and hips. See how much you can let your knee joints release over the toes without actually coming down in space. That means that your

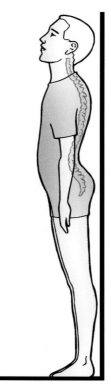

Above Using a wall to achieve better balance and coordination

Using the wall

Look out

Stand around 3 or 4 inches away from the wall with your toes turned out slightly

Inhibit and give your directions for the primary control

Think of an upward release through your ankles, knees and hips

Release up and back from your ankle joints so that you are supported by the wall

Maintain a good heel contact throughout the activity

Allow your knees to release forward from the hip joints and away from each other without losing height or disturbing the balance of your head on your neck

Allow your knees to release a little more so that you come down the wall

To return to upright, let your head lead the body, allow your knees to release a little way apart, directing the ankles towards one another, and slowly move up the wall without stiffening or tightening

head should stay where it is. Now allow your knees to bend forward from your hip joints and away from each other a little or a lot more, maintaining a good heel contact. This will lower your height but you should, of course, maintain a direction for a release up along your spine. A word of warning: it is very important that you do not directly attempt to flatten your back at any point in the procedure. Your spine will lengthen as a function of your legs releasing out of the hip joints, while your back is supported by the wall and your head is going forwards and up off the top of the spine.

If you suffer from flat feet you can also use this position to achieve a better arch. Keeping your knees flexed and maintaining your directions, I will ask you to allow your knees to rotate or spiral outwards away from each other at the same time as you direct your ankles to release towards one another as a counterbalance and your toes releasing either away from the front of your heels, or the front of your ankles, or both.

Now it is time to make the return journey. Most of us find this difficult because as we move the tendency is to pull the head back, pull the back in, lift the chest, tighten the legs and arms and lose the heel contact. So keep in mind that you want to prevent these things happening before any movement takes place. Maintain your head direction and then allow your knees to go a little more apart, directing the ankles towards one another and then allow your legs to straighten without stiffening or tightening. Additionally give the direction 'back (or spine) to release up and back' so that you do not push the back in. You will now be at your full height, still supported by your shoulder blades and lower back against the wall, and your heels still in contact with the ground.

Rising to tiptoe

While supported by the wall you can then decide to go on to your toes. Once again inhibit and direct. With your head leading, allow the movement to take place, maintaining contact with the wall. Remain on your toes for a few seconds or longer, making sure that you are not stiffening your ankles, knees, or hip joints in any way, and then slowly return to the ground by letting the ankles release.

An interesting variation when you are on the toes is to allow your knees to slowly bend over the toes, without any loss of height. This generates a dynamic stretch. At the end of the sequence, inhibit and direct again and allow your legs to straighten without bracing back your knees and stiffening your ankles.

When you have finished and returned to the ground, allow yourself to walk away from the wall, your freely poised head leading, by taking a step forward, knee releasing from your hip joint and lower back. It's very important not to push yourself off the wall with your shoulders or buttocks. If you find that this happens, you can be sure you are relying on a habitual kinaesthetic sense rather than direction. Instead, remember your orders for the primary control and allow the movement to work.

You will now be standing in a new way, your body weight evenly balanced on your feet between front and back and side to side. This will offer you new possibilities and experiences in moving forward, backward or sideways. Even if the improvement in your general coordination does not last for very long, at least it will have given you a glimpse of a much more efficient way of standing on two feet.

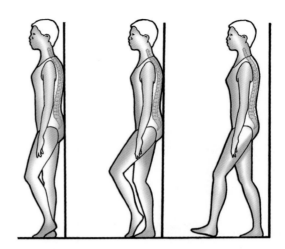

Above Walking away from the wall maintaining balance and coordination

Moving on

I hope the information in this chapter has convinced you that it is worth your while exploring how to stand in a coordinated rather than uncoordinated way. It will, for example, make your life much easier if you can maintain good balance on two feet when you are obliged to wait patiently in a slow-moving queue or stand on a commuter train or bus. Additionally, using inhibition and direction to shift your whole balance up on to the toes will also help you achieve lengthening of the stature and greater stability if you need to retrieve something from a high shelf or cupboard, or want to pick a just out-of-reach apple from a tree.

Above A girl reaching for an apple

And, if you are a dancer, athlete or martial artist, you can take what you have learnt about going on to your toes in standing into more complex activities, since the muscles that you have just activated around your lower legs and feet, especially the toes, are an integral part of the propulsive force required in different types of movement, such as walking, running and jumping.

Above A Taekwondo martial artist performing an aerial kick

A key point here is that it is clear that as a species we have evolved to move rather than remain still for any length of time. Modern sedentarism, characterised by extensive periods of minimal movement, rest and low energy expenditure is a highly unusual development in human history. Before the Industrial Revolution, apart from social elites who used animals, and sometimes other humans, for transportation, most of the population had little or no option but to travel by foot. Even today in traditional societies and many rural and low-income urban areas in the developing world, that remains the case. Which is why we now turn to walking.

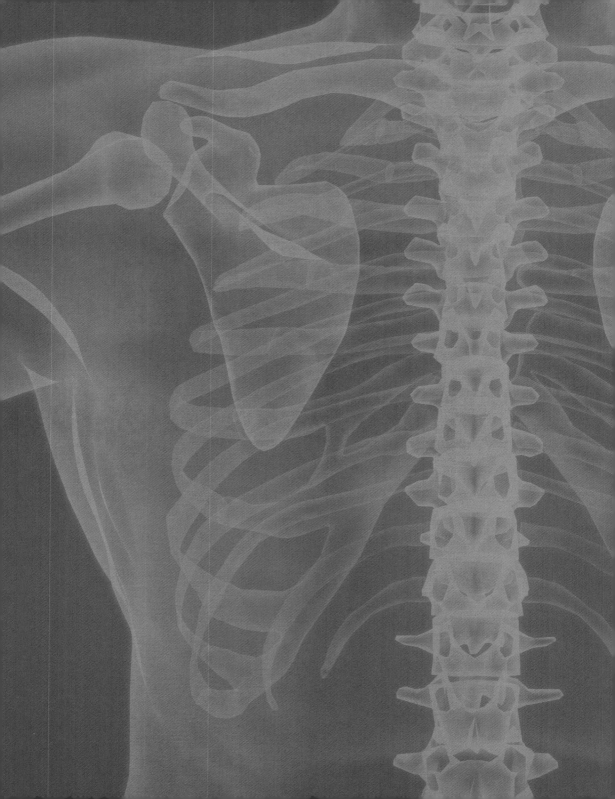

Chapter 5 – *Walking*

'Mr Alexander has done a service ... by insistently treating each act as involving the whole integrated individual, the whole psychophysical man. To take a step is an affair, not of this or that limb solely, but of the total neuromuscular activity of the moment – not least of the head and neck'

Sir Charles Sherrington

'Walking upright on two legs is a defining feature that makes us human. It distinguishes our entire lineage from other apes'

Herman Pontzer

Spiral movements

'He looks as if he is serving around the corner of an imaginary building,' wrote Clive James of John McEnroe, when the US tennis star was in his prime and playing at Wimbledon. Australia's most celebrated cultural critic was, of course, playing it for laughs, but that observation about the way McEnroe, a left-handed player, who won seven Grand Slam titles, uses his body to send a tennis ball hurtling to his opponent reveals a significant truth about the way humans are constructed, in particular the way our body's muscle spirals allow us to move. Without them we would not be going anywhere, or be able to do very much at all.

Above John McEnroe about to serve

When you lengthen in stature all muscular movements are performed with a considerable degree of symmetry and efficiency. But when you shorten in stature the opposite pattern occurs – muscular movements become asymmetrical and inefficient to a greater or lesser extent. Compression of the body's musculature is not like compressing the piston in a car engine, which is smooth and mechanically efficient. Instead, because of the body's inherent flexibility someone losing height will generate any number of distortions and twists. In some people the twisting of the spine is so extensive and visible that it is given a name, scoliosis, by doctors. But the truth is that most of us suffer to a greater or lesser extent from often symptomless scoliosis-type conditions in the neck, head and back, which then create further asymmetries in the legs and arms, which, in turn, feed back into the torso and neck, adversely affecting the working of the primary control.

Lateralisation matters

Allowance must also be made for the fact that in some respects humans are built asymmetrically. In our embryonic development, for example, the heart turns to the left, the liver to the right, while the right and left lungs end up with different shapes, weights and capacities. Brains are also structured into right and left hemispheres and at least in some aspects work asymmetrically. For example, in most people language function is located in the brain's left hemisphere, while paying attention to visual and spatial stimuli is more active on the right.

Although the precise cause of many of these diverse patterns is poorly understood, in terms of initiating movement it is abundantly clear that we have a strong bias either towards the left or the right.

'Put your best foot forward,' the children at my secondary school were told by the teacher-in-charge at the end of the school assembly, which sums up very well that preference we all have for moving one leg and arm over the other (though as we shall see later that particular exhortation lends itself to over striding). Amplify that pattern of one-sidedness for a range of everyday activities – the choice of hand to control your computer, television remote, mobile phone, how you wash dishes, use a knife to chop vegetables, pick up and wield a baseball bat or golf club and which foot you prefer to kick a football with – and it can certainly lead to a pattern of asymmetry and malcoordination, and a range of problems, some minor, some very significant.

The evolutionary significance of walking

Although humans share a rolling heel through to toe movement, with a relatively small number of other animals, including primates such as bonobos, chimpanzees and gorillas, and mammals such as bears and red pandas, we are the only species that is fully upright when walking.

Uprightness even affects breathing. Amongst quadrupeds, for example, there is a direct correlation between locomotion and the respiratory cycle. The thorax of animals such as cats, dogs and horses need to be synchronised with gait to be capable of absorbing the impact of the forelimbs striking the ground in running. In bipeds that relationship has been uncoupled so that movement of the rib cage works relatively independently of striding. One happy consequence of this respiratory plasticity is we can walk and talk at the same time.

Above A baby gorilla demonstrates bipedal walking

While some great apes, such as bonobos, chimpanzees and gorillas, can only manage bipedal walking on the ground with a swaying, relatively rigid body, using bent ankles and knees and a forward-sloping trunk over short distances, human primates, by contrast, are capable of walking by employing extended leg joints in combination with an easy, energy-efficient rotation of a vertically-oriented torso over long distances. So much so that between 80,000 and 130,000 years ago a few thousand anatomically modern humans walked out of Africa into the Middle East and created the opportunity for their descendants to spread out across Europe, Asia and North America before heading south (some reaching Australia by boat around 40,000 years ago).

The ability of our vertically-oriented trunk to rotate is particularly significant. When we walk forward or backward, the spine should twist and turn, rather like the movement you will see if you observe someone wringing water from a wet towel by holding it at each end and turning it in opposite directions. It's through this contra-rotation that some scientists believe that the spine triggers movement in the limbs. From this perspective the vertebral column can be viewed, as the bio-mechanist Serge Gracovetsky claims in his 1988 book *The Spinal Engine*, as the primary generator for locomotion within a constant gravitational field. Indeed, it's interesting that Dr Gracovetsky's theory was inspired, in part, by his observation that people without limbs, who use the sitting bones as 'feet' to move, resemble the pattern of walking used by able-bodied subjects.

The primary control and the spiral mechanism

Yet the discovery by Alexander of a primary control in humans, which predates Gracovetsky's observations by almost a century, demonstrates very clearly that the spine, in conjunction with the rest of the torso and the neck and head, has a dynamic, reciprocal relationship with the limbs. And the insights of Raymond Dart, who by identifying bipedal *Australopithecus africanus* as a separate genus and species, established Africa rather than Europe or the Far East as the cradle of mankind, also need to be taken into account.

After his and his nine-year-old brain-injured son, Galen's, lessons in the Alexander Technique, which began in 1943, Dart began to consider what he later called 'the spiral mechanism of the body'. Around the same time he also reflected on the muscular asymmetries which seemed to be an important component of his 10-year-old daughter Diana's night terrors. This prompted Dart to analyse the way in which congenital or learned asymmetries in the relationship between the head, neck and trunk have a profound effect on behaviour, including our interlinked breathing patterns and emotional responses and the extent to which inappropriate muscular twisting can be modified through conscious inhibition, direction and movement. He published several papers on the subject from the mid-1940s onwards. Interestingly, Alexander read Dart's early essays and was impressed by their theoretical content and perspective.

According to Dart the unique ability of humans to perform complex rotational movements occurs because of the way the flexor and extensor muscles of the trunk form two interwoven, multi-layered sheets – a double spiral musculature – around the bony framework provided by the rib cage and pelvis. The result is that as one spiral contracts, the equal and opposite spiral can release. Practically speaking the spirals connect the base of the skull (the occiput and mastoid processes) and neck vertebrae in a double corkscrew-like pattern through the torso and then out to the legs, feet and toes and arms, hands and fingers. Simply put, in someone with good coordination the double spiral musculature pulls and releases in equal and balanced directions throughout the whole body.

When the primary control is working well movements, including walking and running, take place with great efficiency – 'the right thing does itself' to use Alexander's apt phrase. But a problem arises if you move when over contracting the upper body's spiral musculature. That creates pressures on the entire musculoskeletal system, especially around the lumbar area. This interference in the efficient working of the primary control goes a long way in explaining why people who habitually shorten in stature may experience acute or chronic bouts of lower back pain.

In fact some scientists, unfamiliar with the work of Dart or Alexander, interpret the widespread incidence of lower back pain in Western society as an inevitable consequence of the unique way we walk – one hip joint and leg moving forward at the same time as the opposite shoulder and arm swing forward. 'This creates a twisting motion and, after millions of twists over time, the discs between the vertebrae begin to wear out and break down resulting in herniated discs,' argues Bruce Latimer. 'In addition, age-related bone loss, osteoporosis, the brittle bone disease, also a human condition, further complicates problems.'

Certainly the relative fragility of our spinal health has been highlighted by recent research in the field of evolutionary medicine, in which it was found that young adult humans have larger but more delicate vertebrae, compared with other primates with a similar body mass such as young adult chimpanzees, gorillas, orangutans and gibbons. The light, human spinal column, which evolved as an adaptation to the habitual bipedalism of our early ancestors, bestows a great advantage when upright. There is a downside, however. Light, porous vertebrae have a much thinner outer shell of bone which leaves them vulnerable to cracks and breaks as we age and lose bone density, something which does not occur in other older great apes.

Leaving aside the complex implications of osteoporosis, from an Alexander Technique perspective it is obvious that the twisting motion of the trunk, especially in walking, can actually contribute to the maintenance of a healthy spine, or alternatively to age-related degeneration. The outcome depends in large part on whether, as you go about your daily activities, you are either maintaining or losing height – in other words spiralling upwards, or stiffening downwards.

Exploring spirals in movement

Before we look at walking in more detail it would be a good idea to get some insight into the working of the double spiral musculature which underpins it.

Turning your eyes, turning your body

In order to get a simple but nonetheless powerful experience of your body's spiral mechanism, stand with your feet beneath your head, with the toes turned out slightly. Inhibit and give your orders for primary control. Ensure also that you have a good heel contact with the ground and that you are not bracing back or collapsing your knees, or stiffening your arms. Always remember that you want the muscles of your neck to release and lengthen towards the back of your head, which in turn should be releasing forward and upward throughout the activity. I will monitor what is going on with my hands.

Decide which way you want to turn. Because of lateralisation you will find that you favour one side rather than the other, so you can play around with selection. Let's say that you wish to turn to the right. Look out, pause and then allow only your eyes to look slowly in the direction of your right shoulder. Then maintain the lengthening of stature, release or un-grip your neck to allow your head to turn slowly to follow the direction intended by the eyes so that you are now looking at the right shoulder. If you have not stiffened or lost height, I will ask you to carry on turning with your shoulders following your neck, following your head, following your eyes, which in turn triggers a response further down in your torso and pelvis and finally into your legs and feet.

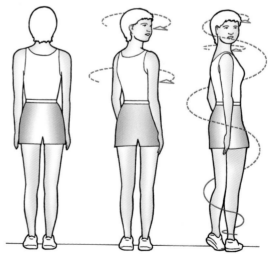

Above Allowing the eyes to initiate movement using the spiral mechanism of the body

Recruitment of the spiral musculature must come in sequence, with your eyes, controlled by the optic nerve, leading the movement. When you have completed the activity, your eyes will have led you to face the opposite direction from where you started, with your feet maintaining an open contact with the floor from which your muscle spirals stretch up and away. If you wish you can reverse the process by allowing your eyes to look slowly towards your left shoulder, carry on turning so that you end up where you started. Working with this procedure will allow you to understand that you rotate three-dimensionally and are not a two-dimensional straight up-and-down being.

Now let's look at another activity exploring your body's spiral mechanism.

Experiencing the spiral mechanism in moving forward

Look out and then inhibit and give the orders for your primary control. With the backs of your hands facing forward slightly, thumbs towards the body, add on a thought for your fingers to lengthen. You can then open your hands, which will help to generate extra release and freedom in the musculature of your arms and shoulders. Select a spot on the wall in front of you – or if you are outdoors a tree or other object – more or less at chest height. Now without raising your shoulders allow your hands to swing forward to touch gently together at the vertical midpoint of your body at around chest height. I will make sure that the movement forward of your arms does not result in lifting or narrowing your chest, pulling in your lower back and displacing your pelvis forward.

Once you have performed this a few times allow each arm in turn, with the thumb leading, to move back and down in space and then return in the direction of your selected spot. Keep your neck free, allow your head to release up and away from the front of your heels, being careful not to stiffen your legs or hold your breath and you will find that your torso is freely contra-rotating. Allow that spiral movement in your upper body to travel into

Above Keeping your head freely poised allows a spiral movement in your body

your legs and feet. Now increase the speed at which your arms are moving back and down by directing your backward-heading thumbs to move more quickly. As long as you are not stiffening you will release up and forward from your ankles. At an appropriate moment I will ask you to stop moving your arms, and allow them to hang by your sides.

Pause momentarily, maintaining your directions, especially to your head, neck and back, while keeping the heel contact and then if you wish walk forward towards the spot you have chosen. I know from experience that although it does not work for everyone, those who have a reasonable degree of muscular elasticity will experience dramatic propulsion for a few paces as the body's short-term muscle memory is activated.

We have explored spirals and their use as a foundation in walking. Now let's consider the origins and benefits of walking.

Out of the trees and on to the ground

Walking on two legs is a highly complex movement requiring coordination between the head, trunk and limbs. Adults take it very much for granted. We tend to forget that as children it took several years for us to gain proficiency in walking because of the sophisticated, slow-developing neuromuscular mechanisms involved.

But how did our species evolve from predominantly tree-dwelling quadrupeds to upright bipeds? The dominant theory in evolutionary biology and palaeoanthropology is that the origins of bipedal walking lay in the periods of significant climatic shifts and environmental changes affecting Africa between five and 10 million years ago. A period of cooling and drying reduced the size of the central African rainforest, resulting in a decrease in the amount of fruit available, propelling ape-like creatures living on the outer fringes of the forest to supplement their diet by foraging for other types of plant food

Above A group of Hadza women

such as leaves, stems and herbs in more open woodland or savannah environments. In turn that led to anatomical changes, since ape-like creatures which were able to stand upright and later on to walk upright and cover large amounts of ground would have gained a considerable advantage in foraging over those restricted to knuckle-walking. Over time natural selection resulted in biomechanically efficient walking on two feet becoming the norm, and led to our early ancestors taking a separate evolutionary path from the chimpanzee lineage.

As a consequence our forebears walked a lot in the search for food. Not surprisingly the same is true of contemporary hunter-gatherers such as the Hadza people. Because storage is not used to any great extent every day Hadza men, women and older children journey outside the temporary camps located near waterholes in order to forage for a wide variety of foodstuffs. Researchers have found that on average women will spend around four hours and men six hours walking each day. To protect their feet from thorns and sharp rocks, many Hadza foragers use thin-soled sandals (about 1 cm thick) without cushioning or elevated heels. Traditionally these sandals were made from impala skin, but nowadays are increasingly fashioned from discarded rubber tyres.

Modern day hunter-gatherers provide important clues as to the importance of walking for the survival of Homo sapiens, including its role in maintaining health and preventing obesity. For example, a recent study of the Hadza foragers found that women who wandered each day over hilly terrain gathering berries, vegetable tubers and other plants, often while carrying water, firewood and young children, walked on average 3.6 miles (5.8 km) a day, while men who tend to hunt alone or in groups for game and forage for honey, covered 7.08 miles (11.4 km).

What surprised a team of researchers from New York's Hunter College, however, was that despite differences in physical activity between the male and female Hadza and relatively inactive, sedentary workers in Europe and North America, there was little or no difference in overall metabolic rates between the groups even allowing for differences in body size, gender and age. 'This to me says that the big reason that Westerners are getting fat is because we eat too much – it's not because we exercise too little,' says evolutionary anthropologist Herman Pontzer. 'Daily energy expenditure might be an evolved trait that has been shaped by evolution and is common among all people and not some simple reflection of our diverse lifestyles.'

On the other hand, there is no suggestion from the scientists that walking is a waste of time and that we might as well sit in front of the computer or lie in bed all day. 'Being active is really important to your health,' explains Dr Pontzer highlighting the importance of walking for the maintenance of cognitive functioning, bone density and the prevention of Type 2 diabetes, stroke, heart disease and some cancers.

Another study by the US National Cancer Institute, which analysed pooled data of more than 650,000 people from six previous studies (one in Sweden and five in the US) found that 75 minutes of brisk walking a week was associated with an increase in life expectancy of 1.8 years among subjects over the age of 40, compared with those who were inactive. And this correlation was true for those of normal weight, overweight and the obese, men and women, and among blacks and whites. Those walking briskly between 150 and 299 minutes a week increased their life expectancy between 3.4 and 4.5 years. The researchers led by Dr Steven Moore concluded: 'This result may help convince currently inactive people that a modest physical activity program may have health benefits, even if it does not result in weight loss.'

The general consensus based on contemporary scientific research is that walking is highly beneficial, not only because of its cardiovascular benefits but also because of its mood-regulating effects. For example, it helps to stave off or reduce depression and anxiety, partly by releasing the stress hormone adrenaline stored in muscles, and partly by stimulating circulation and breathing. Walking also has been shown to reduce the risk of dementia by around 20 per cent, improve sleep quality and contributes to whole-body bone density. Yet whatever the motivation and benefits, the important question from an Alexander Technique point of view is: what methods should you employ in walking to make it as efficient as possible in order to get positive health benefits without incurring damage or injury to your musculoskeletal system?

Alexander's perspective on walking – the importance of the first step

In a brief account of walking in his first book *Man's Supreme Inheritance*, Alexander complained about the widespread tendency of 'civilised peoples' to adopt a 'rolling gait' (side-to-side movement). 'Nearly everyone I examine or observe in the act of walking,' he wrote, 'employs unnecessary physical tension in the process in such a way that there is a tendency to shorten the spine and legs, by pressing . . . down through the floor.'

The 'rolling gait' detected by Alexander was most likely the dominant pattern of walking amongst middle-class Edwardian Londoners. In fact making a side-to-side swaying movement remains remarkably prevalent amongst people in contemporary Europe and North America, although nowadays it is matched by a pattern of over striding, in which the foot lands too far ahead of the trunk, the head is pulled down on to the neck, the lower back is pulled in and the rib cage stiffened. This pattern of malcoordination in part reflects the amount of time many of us spend in slumped, C-shaped sitting, a practice which causes contraction throughout the body's musculature and interferes with our proprioceptive sense (more on this in Chapter 6), but also in part reflects or expresses the absorption by our body-minds of the hard-to-escape time pressures embedded in post-industrial societies.

When Alexander made that observation about a rolling gait he reckoned that the basis of efficient walking was to start by placing one foot a little way either behind or in front of the other making an angle of about 45 degrees between the feet, with the body weight mainly supported by the rear foot. This allows the knee of the forward leg to bend so that a small step can be taken with the front foot. At the same time, the ankle of the rear foot should bend a little so that, as Alexander explained, 'the whole body is inclined slightly forward, thus allowing the propelling force of gravitation to be brought into play'. With a lengthening, supportive torso the transition from standing into walking is, he added, 'really resolved into the primary movements of allowing the body to incline forward from the ankle on which the weight is supported and in preventing oneself from falling by allowing the weight be taken in turn by the foot which has been advanced'. It's well worth you experimenting with this.

Later on in life Alexander had simplified and refined what was required sometimes saying to a student at the end of a lesson: 'Up to put the foot down because we all think down to put the foot down.' It's a succinct summary of what's involved in biomechanically efficient locomotion. That insight, however, needs to be unpacked so that you have enough information to be able to make walking both efficient and pleasurable.

Above A group of friends walking

Inclining up and forward

The original point Alexander made about the importance of maintaining extension in the torso and an up and forward lean from the ankles in standing *before* initiating the movement into walking remains key for efficient walking. So, place both feet underneath your head, your heels a couple of inches or so apart from each other with the toes turned out very slightly (no need for a 45 degree angle between your feet). Inhibit and give your directions for the primary control and add a direction for an upward release through your ankles, knees and hips. Also direct your shoulders, arms and hands to release as this will help to generate a better and more defined use of your body's cross-pattern spiral musculature when you move.

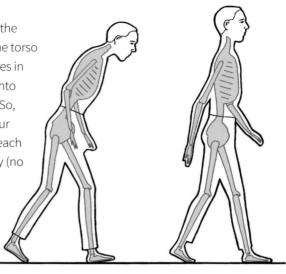

Above Although we can walk in many different ways it is far better for us to walk efficiently

Of course while standing on two feet it is possible to actively lean forward from your ankles to go into walking. The danger, however, is that the direction so generated will be forward and *down*. You will pull your head down on to your neck and compress your body. It's much better, then, to stand and *think* of leaning up and forward from your ankles while maintaining contact of the heels with the floor as if you were going to go up on to the toes (you can refer to Chapter 4). That direction will help bring you into a state of lengthening upright balance.

Keep your primary direction of up and forward going and let, say, your left knee release forward from the hip joint so that the heel of your left foot peels gently away from the ground without disturbing the supportive balance provided by both of your legs. Allow that to continue until you are on the tip of your big toe and then let the foot leave the floor. (Alternatively, you can organise the movement by allowing your left heel to peel off the floor so that your left knee extends over and beyond the toes.) Your left leg will swing forward and your foot will land with a gentle, rolling movement, the front of your heel making contact with the ground just before the forefoot. Allow your body to continue moving forward and, departing from the big toe of your right foot, you will have taken one more step and then another and another. That pattern of movement will activate the appropriate contra-rotation around your spinal axis, your arms also playing their part. You are now walking without swaying, rolling or displacing your pelvis forward or sideways or over striding. Keeping your ankle joints free will also result in your feet being able to adjust to whatever type of surface you happen to be walking on.

Keeping it simple

It might seem that there is a lot to think about, but in reality Alexander walking is relatively simple. Look out, give the directions for your primary control and limbs and then add on a direction for a lean up and forward from your 'open' ankle joints while you maintain contact with your heels, direct your knee forward so that it releases out of your hip joint (or allow your heel to peel off the floor) and take a step, while allowing your body's spiral mechanism to work. The result will be that you will move with a spring in your step. Your intention about where you wish to go will carry you forward without any need to micromanage the movement until you stop.

The process of walking

As you continue to move forward, as well as maintaining a freely poised head and lengthening torso, you will want to continue to pay attention to the thought of an upward release through your ankles, knees and hips so that the three leg joints remain available for movement (note that stiffness in one joint will promote stiffness in the other two). This will promote a circular-type movement in your legs, almost like the turning of a bicycle wheel.

When walking you will also want to remember to look out and take in your surroundings, using the horizon as a reference point. If, however, you find that when walking you are not 'present' because of internal mental chatter, you might find it helpful to say the directions aloud. Hearing the words often helps shift attention, bringing you into the here and now.

If you experience a sense of becoming heavy and flat-footed, you can try to direct in process by reducing your speed since a slower movement tends to provide better kinaesthetic

> ### *Thinking about walking*
>
> *Look out*
>
> *Inhibit and give your directions for the primary control*
>
> *Think of an upward release through your ankles, knees and hips*
>
> *Place your feet a little way apart with the toes turned out very slightly*
>
> *Maintain contact with the ground with the front of your heels*
>
> *Think of leaning up and forward from your ankles while maintaining your heel contact*
>
> *Allow either your right or left knee to release forward from a free hip joint and a lengthening and widening back*
>
> *Allow your body's natural contra-rotations to work but do not try to 'do' them*

feedback. Alternatively, stop, give your directions, especially the direction of an upward release along the spine into your head around eye level, and add on an order to release up and forward from your ankle joints. You can then begin walking again. If that does not work,

Walking backwards

As we have already seen one of the most common forms of misuse in walking is pulling in the lumbar region of the back, while lifting the chest as a precursor to the knees moving upward. It's often difficult to know which element of malcoordination comes first. In a way, it does not really matter because it is the total pattern of misuse that needs to be addressed. But certainly if you take too long a stride, especially on the first step, it will cause problems. Your pelvis will be displaced forward, in advance of the moving foot, and you will have to lean back from somewhere in your middle back as a counterbalance to prevent yourself falling over.

An effective way of overcoming the tendency to over stride is to explore walking backwards. Although popular as a form of exercise in China and Japan, retro-walking as it is now called is not a movement familiar to most Westerners. Partly for that reason, it creates an opportunity to perform a movement without triggering a habitual response.

Falling backwards from the ankle joints will certainly generate movement but is not advisable as most of us will stiffen because of the fear of falling. There are better ways to start. First, I will ask you to stand with your feet close together underneath your head, and with the toes turned out slightly. Look out, inhibit and give your directions. If necessary achieve a balance on your feet by coming back in small movements from your ankles joints as described in Chapter 4. Now **think** *of leaning up and back from your ankles in conjunction with directing your spine up and back and your head forward and up, before allowing your left or right leg to release from the hip joint, so that your heel peels off the floor and you take a step backwards.*

In contrast with walking forward, it will not be your heel but the toes of your moving foot that will first contact the ground, followed by the ball of the foot and then the front of the heel in such a way that your lumbar region moves backwards at the same speed as your chosen heel. Then allow your other leg and foot to release backwards, once again in coordination with your lower back moving rearwards.

As in walking forward, your weight will be supported in a balanced way as you travel backwards as long as you maintain the directions for the primary control and do not try too big a step. In order to help you understand the importance of the upward direction along your spine, I will provide support with my arm to your upper back as you move back in space.

The second way of organising the movement, although counterintuitive, is one with which you are already familiar in walking forward. Look out, inhibit and direct. Maintain your heel contact and direct as if you were going up on to the toes. That thought will help to generate lengthening, internal springiness and better balance. From that attitude, simply allow your right or left knee to release forward from your hip joint and supportive torso, avoiding any displacement of the pelvis, before taking a small step backwards.

Once you are moving backwards in balance you have some options. First, you can stop walking, bring your feet underneath your head, and then walk forward. Second, if there is sufficient space, you can carry on walking backwards, and then allow your eyes to turn towards one of your shoulders, followed by your head and then your torso, in such a way that the movement continues and flows through your pelvis into your legs so that you are now walking forward while maintaining your internal length.

The key lesson in walking is that the upward movement along your spine precedes any movement forward, backwards or, indeed, in any other direction. Lengthening up through your body really is the primary movement which allows all other movements to take place efficiently and effectively.

it probably means that you are overtired. In that case, it is time to let the train, bus, taxi or whatever take the strain.

The role of your shoulders and arms

Many of us find that we hunch our shoulders when walking, especially if we are moving quickly. Instead of the column of the neck releasing up out of the torso it is stiffened and shortened, while the shoulder girdle, which should hang from the vertebrae of the spine, is actually pulled upwards. To avoid this, it is a good idea to remember that your shoulders are an integral part of your torso. An effective way for you to think about this is to direct your shoulder blades to lie flat on your back. It's complemented by giving an order to maintain space in your armpits, which facilitates release outwards through your shoulder girdle. These directions are also useful when you are walking up and down stairs, an activity in which nearly everyone stoops or loses height.

Many people also find that they also habitually hold the arms stiff when walking. This is a waste of energy. Because of the complex neural connections operating between your upper and lower limbs any interference in the arms will have a marked effect on the efficiency of your stride pattern and balance. As you have already learnt in standing the simplest way to avoid stiffening your arms is to give the directions for your head, neck and back, and then add on a thought for your shoulders to widen away from each other, and allow your elbows to release and open towards the ground. The same directions also work in walking, although this time in conjunction with a rhythmic twisting around your spinal axis. It's also important that your slightly forward-facing hands remain open and your fingers, especially the thumbs, are directed to release into length.

Walking and carrying objects

People often make walking difficult by carrying objects – newspapers, bags, or mobile phones, for example – using tight, clenched hands. If you are going to carry something,

Above Carrying a bag or other items can interfere with balanced walking by encouraging us to lean to one side make sure that your hands are directed to release into length and width before taking hold of the object. Additionally, use a hook grip or extensor grip whenever possible (we cover the latter in Chapter 8). Some of us try to get round the problem of carrying objects in our hands by using rucksacks. But these too can cause interference because their shape can interfere with the contra-rotations in the torso. If you do use a rucksack make sure that it is not too bulky and is carried as high on your back as the straps will allow, and not draped low down, as this will tend to push your lumbar curve forward.

Above Two Hadza hunters walking back to camp with the day's catch

Walking as exercise

The best way to promote free walking with optimum use of your body's spiral mechanism is to move for around 20 to 30 minutes each day – more if you have the time – without carrying anything and giving the directions for the primary control.

The aim when walking in everyday life should not just be seen as a method of going from A to B but also something that facilitates release rather than creating unnecessary muscular tension. Because of the widely-recognised health risks associated with a sedentary lifestyle, many health authorities in the Western world suggest that walking should be looked at as 'moderate-intensity aerobic exercise' – that is you should move fast enough to raise your heartbeat and break into a light sweat.

There is nothing wrong with walking at speed, but there is little point in performing it by stiffening and losing height. One way of achieving balanced Alexander walking is not to walk too quickly at the outset. This is not what usually happens as you can see when people go about their daily business. For example, when commuters disembark from trains, trams and buses most are in a desperate hurry.

Unfortunately achieving speed often comes at the expense of internal length – the head will be thrown back, chest lifted, back pinched and narrowed, pelvis displaced forward, with ankles, knees and hips stiffened because of an over stride. Of course it creates internal noise – 'I can feel I'm making a lot of effort, so I must be moving fast'. The reality is that this is just an illusion. It's a very good example of a faulty kinaesthetic sense. It would be much better for you to start by achieving balance in standing before moving forward slowly and then give a direction for an increase in the degree of up and forward lean from your ankle joints to achieve a smooth and controlled acceleration.

Coming to a stop

If you walk in the country or on the coast you can often walk for hours without stopping. But those of us who live or work in urban spaces are very aware that the experience of walking is frequently interrupted by the pattern of the built environment and the presence of other people. Nevertheless wherever you are walking and have to stop, you want to ensure that you do not stiffen or tighten. Maintaining the directions for your primary control will help you maintain good balance, so that even if you do have to swerve or stop unexpectedly, it is possible to avoid losing height. While you are standing waiting for the opportunity to move again it is a good idea to keep the directions for your head, neck and back in mind as well as orders for an upward release through your ankles, knees and hips. Your feet should be releasing into the ground opposing the crown of your head which is directed skywards.

Footwear

The use of footwear is a relatively recent development in human history. The world's oldest preserved shoes were constructed from sagebrush bark fibre by Native Americans keen to insulate themselves against snow and freezing temperatures in the Pacific Northwest around 10,500 years ago (though it seems likely that sandals were used by both modern humans and Neanderthals in parts of Europe and Asia some 30,000 years before that). Many contemporary populations living in warm climates in the developing world never wear shoes. Such barefoot people tend to have wide feet, pronounced arches and more evenly distributed plantar pressure. By contrast, habitual shoe wearers have narrower feet, exhibit very high focal pressures at the heel, big toe and ball of the foot, and often suffer anatomical abnormalities, such as weak toes, bunions and flat feet.

Walking barefoot *really* is the gold standard. Why? Well the sensory nerves on the bottom of our feet provide important proprioceptive information about the ground we are walking on. This process is made more difficult if shoes are worn – and the more cushioned or stiffer the shoes, the worse the problem. Even socks interfere with this proprioceptive process. For most of us, barefoot walking is best performed on natural surfaces like grass and sand, or indoors.

Above Children should maximise the time spent barefoot

It's also especially important to maximise the time that children spend barefoot so that their feet can develop without distortion or deformities.

On the other hand walking barefoot is not very practical or comfortable if carried out when it is cold and wet. Furthermore, in our affluent, culturally complex society footwear is a form of customary behaviour. (When was the last time you saw anyone walking barefoot in public, except on holiday?) Although a shoe keeps the foot warm, dry and provides protection from sharp objects, it also says something about you and the situation which you are in. As we know the accepted dress code for shoes is not the same when jogging in the local park as when attending a wedding.

Shoes are also used to mark social distinctions, including those associated with gender. High heels are particularly significant in this regard. In one form or another they have been around for centuries. In 1595 Queen Elizabeth I commissioned a pair of elaborately decorated shoes with wooden high heels and arches covered in leather known as chopines. Although they increased instability and awkwardness in movement, these shoes were the height of fashion amongst Italian and Spanish noblewomen, who had adopted the style from contemporary Venetian prostitutes, keen to increase their height, visibility and perceived attractiveness. In previous centuries high-platform shoes were also worn by Chinese and Turkish concubines.

Today many women in Western societies wear high heels on social occasions and at work, simply because they are fashionable. However, evidence suggests that extensive use of such footwear, especially ultra-high heels, is linked with significant physical problems. It's associated with a marked shortening of the highly malleable muscle fibres that make up the calves as well as thicker and stiffer Achilles tendons. Long-term use of high heels is also correlated with the development of on-going foot pain, restriction in the ankle's range of movement and weakness of the toes. Unsurprisingly those problems show up more in ageing adults. Yet these widely recognised health problems have had little or no impact on the choices of footwear made by women in Western societies.

What footwear would you choose if you had to walk or run quickly, movements which the human biped has evolved to do very efficiently? Platform shoes, high heels, and flip-flops would not be a good choice, even for the very well-coordinated. They will interfere with your balance and alignment and decrease your potential speed. It's also possible that if you did run flat out wearing inappropriate shoes you might even end up with a sprained ankle, or worse.

The optimum choice is well-fitting shoes with thin, flexible soles that follow the movement of your feet without the need to try to hang on with the toes. Running and other types of sport shoes, without unnecessary and harmful padding, which enable an open contact with the ground, will suit most of us, especially if we are doing a reasonable amount of walking as part of our everyday routine. If the heels of your sports shoes are too high one way to partially solve the problem is to remove the insoles.

To sum up: it is probably best to wear a pair of Christian Louboutin heels (or other types of stiff-soled footwear) only on very special occasions. If you do put them on try to walk on the balls of your feet rather than landing on the heels (we cover this in Chapter 4) – though be aware that you are using around 50 per cent more energy compared with a normal heel-sole-toe action.

Above Christian Louboutin's brand of high heels

A word on the weather

All of us are aware that our pattern of movement in walking changes if it is raining or cold. The tendency is to hunch up to get protection from the elements. But the truth as scientists have discovered in experiments examining people adopting various body poses when it is raining is that you will not get significantly less wet if you try to make yourself smaller. You will not get any warmer either. In fact tightening your muscles and preventing the efficient contra-rotation of your torso and limbs means that you are actively interfering with your circulation. The best thing when it is raining or cold is to wear suitable, protective clothing, including gloves to keep your hands warm.

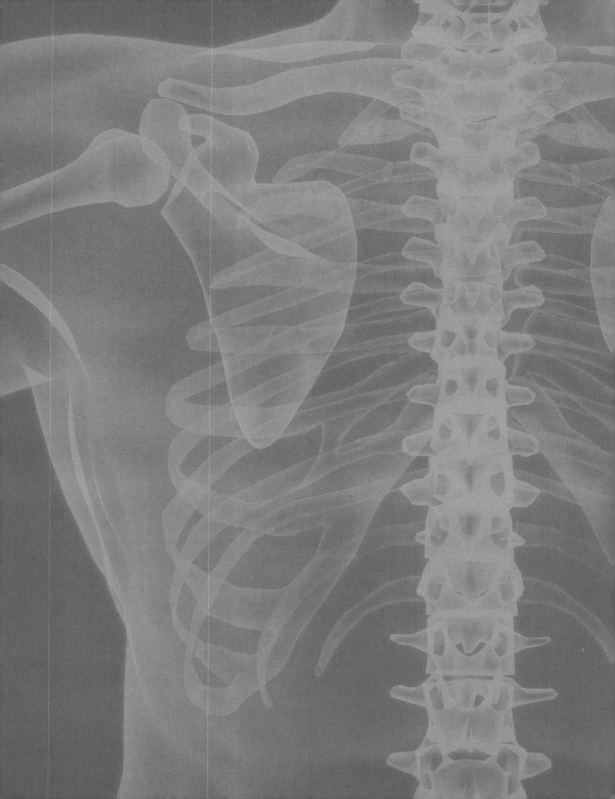

Chapter **6** – *Sitting*

'It is my opinion that habitual use of improper reflex
mechanisms in sitting, standing and walking introduces
conflict in the nervous system, and that this conflict
is because of fatigue and nervous strain which
bring many ills in their train'

George E Coghill

'Being endowed with prominent rounded buttocks
is the unique privilege of humans. Old World monkeys
and apes sit on bony plates covered with corneal tissue,
the ischial tuberosities, which protrude through the fur.
The human buttocks are made of soft cushions composed
of a thick muscular layer – the 'gluteus maximus'
– topped by a mattress of subcutaneous
adipose tissue covered with smooth skin'

Françoise K Jouffroy and Monique F Médina

In December 1940 Alexander travelled from his New York teaching base to spend the weekend at the home of Professor George E Coghill in Gainesville, Florida to provide an intensive introduction to the technique. 'To think that you and I have worked in our different ways and come to the same conclusions,' the 68-year-old award-winning anatomist and physiologist told Alexander at the end of the first lesson. Then, his eyes brimming with tears, he added: 'But, whereas it's made you, it's destroyed me.' Coghill's comment was recognition that a lifetime crouched over a microscope in the laboratory investigating the structure and movement patterns of salamanders had wrought havoc on his body and health, whereas by contrast Alexander despite being three years his senior was in the form of his life.

Above A contemporary-style chair

Coghill's encounter with the Alexander Technique made him reflect deeply about the taken-for-granted aspects of a Western-inspired modern lifestyle, in particular the way many of us sit, as well as how we get in and out of a chair. Writing the Appreciation to Alexander's fourth and final book, *The Universal Constant in Living*, first published in 1941, Coghill did not mince his words. The chair, he said, was 'the most atrocious institution hygienically of civilised life'. Whereas efficient squatting involves a release and stretching of the extensor muscles of the legs through a movement of the knees forward from the hip joints and away from each other, using a chair in sitting often prevents this happening. To make matters worse, according to Coghill, some people even go to the 'extreme of crossing one leg over the other'. The effects were clear to the sharp-eyed scientist. 'Habitual use of the chair… tends to stimulate reflex responses which antagonize the normal total pattern of rising to a standing position,' he concluded.

The rise in popularity of the chair

Historically, and still today in many societies, people rest or work by sitting on the floor. One considerable advantage of this attitude is that our bodies experience greater stability compared with standing. In turn that stability facilitates a complex range of manual skills. This is certainly true of the Hadza hunter-gatherers. When not foraging or sleeping Hadza spend their time in temporary camps, sitting or squatting on the ground, socialising and working.

Above Three Hadza young men sitting on rocks

But the numbers of traditional peoples who squat, sit or kneel on the ground, like our forebears, are a small and ever-dwindling number of the world's population. The use of the chair, traditionally a mark of royal and aristocratic status in many agrarian societies, is growing exponentially, especially as people in fast-growing economies such as Indonesia, Mexico and Tanzania move from the countryside to economically dynamic urban centres in the quest for material betterment.

Sitting on a chair

Sitting and well-being

Research carried out by Canadian and Scottish scientists has discovered that how we sit on a chair has enormous implications for health and well-being. The team, which used an innovative whole body MRI scanner to investigate 22 adult volunteers with 'healthy' backs, found at the start of the study that despite being asymptomatic 12 of the group exhibited a significant degree of disc degeneration or disc protrusion. The scans then revealed that sitting on a chair with feet touching the floor in either a forward slouch or an upright 90 degrees, 'good posture' position, had a significant impact on the vertebral column, since the lowest spinal discs in particular were displaced and squashed. Interestingly, the effect was greatest in the sit up 'straight' position. In as little as 10 minutes fluid was leaking out of the inner core of the discs. The reason, as we have already learnt, is that sitting up 'straight' as most people understand it, is just another way of pulling the head down on to the neck, raising the chest and arching the back. In turn, that lifts the sitting bones off the chair and transfers body weight on to the thighs, creating

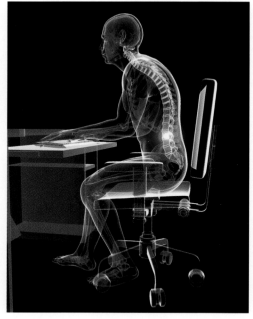

Above Sitting poorly places a great strain on the spine

inappropriate downward pressure along the spinal column. 'Just think of that day in day out, year in year out, you will eventually cause degeneration,' said lead researcher musculoskeletal radiologist Waseem Bashir. For that reason he recommends that people should sit with the feet flat on the ground at an open torso-thigh angle of 135 degrees, the attitude which was found to result in the least amount of spinal disc distortion.

Whilst Dr Bashir is right about the advantages of a reclining position while watching TV or on a long-haul flight, it is obvious that someone will have trouble using a workstation or dining table if positioned so far back. From an Alexander Technique point of view at least some of the conclusions drawn from such studies indicate an overly mechanistic way of looking at the problem. Researchers have not factored in the possibility of us achieving a better general coordination along with an improved kinaesthetic sense. 'We need to change the people, not the furniture,' was how Alexander once summed it up to a student. Indeed, it is possible for you to sit on a chair in a variety of attitudes – that is, at different angles – without damaging your discs, ligaments and muscles as long as your primary control is working well, allowing body weight to be effectively transmitted through your downward-pointing sitting bones and feet, and other support surfaces. That's much better than either trying to sit up 'straight' or slumping.

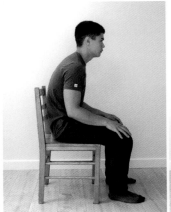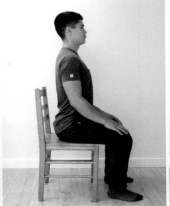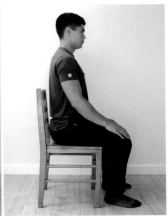

Above There are many different ways to sit on a chair (C-shaped, over straight or in balance, but we need to sit with our weight efficiently transmitted through our sitting bones)

Nevertheless Dr Bashir is right to comment that 'we were meant to be mobile, not to be static. Unfortunately, we have come to this kind of culture where most of the day we're actually more static than we are mobile, we'll sit in a chair all day long, then sit in a car, go home, sit and watch television and go to bed.'

Sitting and standing

'If you ask any of your friends to sit down, you will notice, if you observe their actions closely,' said Alexander, 'that in nearly all cases there is undue increase of muscular tension in the body and lower limbs; in many cases the arms are actually employed. As a rule, however, the most striking action is the alteration in the position of the head, which is thrown back, whilst the neck is stiffened and shortened.'

If you have pulled the head back and down as you went into sitting, you will almost certainly find the same pattern when you stand up. As Alexander perceptively noted: '… in this act of rising, you will observe that in the movement as performed by an imperfectly co-ordinated person the same bad movements occur tending to stiffen the neck, to arch the spine unduly, to shorten the body, and to protrude the abdominal wall.' Of course, there are variations in the way people sit down and stand up, but most follow this pattern.

The stand-to-sit movement has been the subject of research. In the early 1940s, Wilfred Barlow, a first-generation Alexander Technique teacher, who was also a National Health Service (NHS) consultant rheumatologist, carried out an experiment with 105 young men, aged between 17 and 22. Attaching a tape measure to the back of the subjects' heads, and making an ink mark at the seventh cervical vertebra, the bony protuberance where the neck joins the torso at the back, Dr Barlow asked the young men to sit down, and a record was taken of how much the tape measure moved from the ink mark.

The results were extremely revealing. Only one subject did not pull back his head, while 56 moved the tape downwards by two inches or more, 43 between one and two inches and nine under an inch. Interestingly younger members of the sample pulled the head back and down less than older ones, which strongly suggests that there is an age-related aspect to this pattern of behaviour. The 104 students who had pulled their heads back and down when going to sit were then asked to repeat the process without doing so. Only 11 of the group were successful, no matter how hard they tried.

Experimenting with sitting and standing

If you want to find out how you sit down you can use the simple technology employed in the Barlow experiment. Place an elasticated band around the top of the head and attach a tape measure underneath so that it runs down your back. You can then mark the seventh cervical vertebra at the base of your neck if you are doing it without wearing a top, or you can place a sticker on the outside of your clothing at the same point. Ask a friend with a video camera or smartphone to face the tape measure and record what happens when you sit down in your habitual way. If the camera has a slow motion or freeze-frame facility, it will be possible to dissect in more detail what is going on, and in what order, especially what's happening around your head, neck and shoulders.

You can then take the experiment one stage further, and find out what happens when you get out of the chair.

Another simple way of getting a measure of how you sit and stand that you can employ in a variety of other activities in everyday life, is to carefully place your lengthened index finger at the base of the middle part of your skull, without interfering with your shoulders and affecting the balance of your head on the neck. Then monitor what happens when

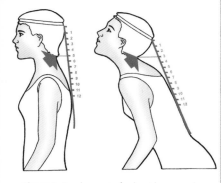

Above A simple way to find out how much you pull your head back

you move. If you pull the head back and down when you sit or stand you will experience a downward pressure on your fingertip. Find out if you can perform the movement without pulling the head back. Be aware that it is best to observe yourself in a mirror so that you are not just relying on feeling.

Coordinated sitting and standing

Two interesting questions are raised by our inability to sit and stand using a chair without pulling the head back and down. First, because stand-to-sit and sit-to-stand movements are normally over in a second or so, it is reasonable to ask: Does it matter? The answer is: Yes, it really does. Sitting and standing without maintaining a proper working of the primary control will inevitably result in significant compression throughout your body. That means that every time you sit and stand and pull your head down on to your neck you are actively compressing the joints throughout the entire length of your body. One consequence is that there is less available space for your vital functions – not only your breathing but also your digestion and circulation. Over time that pattern of repetitive, punctuated compression will almost certainly result in damage to your skeleton, spinal discs, ligaments and muscles. And very importantly, persistent compression (and slouching) also interferes with and degrades your proprioceptive sense, which increases the risk of on-going spinal instability and injury.

Furthermore unless you register what is going on and make some conscious intervention to generate lengthening of the stature the compression you have generated in sitting down will last throughout the period you remain seated. In fact it is likely to get worse because gravity is likely to pull you down even more, especially if fatigue sets in, or you end up sitting for a long time at work, or when you are reading, or chatting with friends. Perhaps pulling ourselves out of shape when sitting down, sitting and standing up would not matter quite so much if it was an occasional occurrence. Alas, it is not. For most of us it is the only way we know how to move.

The second question is: why does compression happen during the acts of sitting and standing? The answer is simple and straightforward from a biomechanical point of view: losing internal length occurs through excessive contraction of the flexor and extensor muscle systems in response to gravity. Although this aberrant pattern of movement is not an evolutionary but a learned response, it is one which becomes deeply embedded in the neuromuscular systems of almost all chair-using adults. In the act of sitting badly, for example, it is reasonable to assume that you consider that your primary task is to get your seat on to or out of the chair by any direct means.

At one level that makes sense. You are standing and you wish to place your pelvis on the chair. Unfortunately, almost everyone starts the movement by tightening the muscles of the neck, which pulls the head back and down. Performing the action in this way takes you off-balance and your brain and nervous system react quickly to mobilise the rest of the musculature to tighten to prevent you falling over. Something very similar happens when you go to stand from a sitting position. You subconsciously think that you have to push yourself 'up' with your legs, typically by pulling them together by misusing the (adductor) muscles on the inside and the back of the thighs, and perhaps also employing your arms, to get to upright. Compounding the problem is that this movement pattern is conceptually reinforced because nearly everyone else you see or meet carries it out in more or less the same way. It's very much a case of when in Rome we all do as the Romans do – although in this particular instance we definitely should not.

Sitting down

So much for how not to sit down. There is, of course, a better way to proceed than losing internal length. That, like everything else in the Alexander Technique, involves inhibition and direction – thinking about the process rather than focusing exclusively on the end point of an activity.

When standing in front of a chair most of us use too narrow a base, which makes it difficult to bend the knees. To obtain a wider stance, I will ask you to inhibit and direct and then put your feet about hip-width apart, maintaining contact with the front of the heels, with the toes turned out slightly. The next thing I am going to ask of you is to suspend the belief that putting your seat on the chair is the most efficient way to accomplish the task. Next, you want to reason out that the best way to end up seated on the chair is to allow your knees to release forward gently and steadily from the hip joints and apart from each other over your feet, while maintaining the directions for the primary control, especially the upward direction from your tailbone to the top of your spine. So look out and allow me to take you slightly up and back from the pivot points of your ankles, and more or less simultaneously let your knees bend. The opposition between your head releasing forward and up, your knees going forward from the hip joints and away from each other over the toes and your back going up and back will activate a whole variety of antagonistic muscular actions, including getting your lower back to engage.

In the act of going to sit your trajectory will be in large part determined both by your directions and the degree of freedom in your body's musculoskeletal system. Unless I previously asked you to place your feet further apart than hip-width, the likelihood is that your descent will not have been completely vertical. After releasing your knees, hips and ankles, and descending to find your first contact with the chair you will now be not only supported by your sitting bones and heels but also inclined forward from the hip joints. In this case I will ask you to pause and give your orders for the primary control, and perhaps additionally give a preventative direction for your tailbone to drop if you are tipping your pelvis. You also need to be careful to maintain a thought of freedom in the legs.

Now allow me to move you quite slowly so that your spine is releasing up and back from your heels to a vertical alignment. This movement will help to activate your body's anti-gravity musculature. It's also very important that you allow the chair to provide support and that you do not, as Alexander pointed out, make 'a further and unnecessary movement on the lines of closing a concertina, ending in a slumped attitude when sitting on the chair.' Your upper body weight will now be taken through downward-pointing sitting bones and your feet will be flat on the floor (if they are raised it means that you are tight in the ankles and calf muscles; do not worry, that is a condition that will get better over time).

The experience of sitting in a lesson will be markedly different from how you habitually carry it out, either because you are slumping, or because you are trying to achieve 'good' posture by sitting up 'straight'. The new attitude may feel odd or strange at first – too 'regal' if you are used to collapsing, or too 'forward' if you try to sit up 'straight', perhaps – but observe yourself in a mirror and you will see that you are sitting in a very balanced way and, in most cases, without a sense of effort because of efficient support from your back musculature.

It's also important to understand that when sitting on a chair it is possible to remain in a balanced and upright state for some considerable time. To help you appreciate the importance of creating and then maintaining an upward direction along the spine from the sitting bones, I will ask you to look out and give the directions for your head, neck, back and hip joints while I use my hands to move your upper body in little circles in either a clockwise or counterclockwise direction, or both. That will provide you with the experience of your torso weight being partially transferred from one seat bone to the other while balance is maintained and breathing continues uninterrupted. It also demonstrates that balancing on your sitting bones with direction is much more than a straight up-and-down affair.

Standing up

Before the movement from sit to stand you need to say 'no' to the idea of moving, especially the notion that getting out of the chair involves pulling your knees together, or even using your arms and hands to push downwards on the thighs or furniture to get lift-off. In fact you can eliminate the latter tendency by resting the backs of your hands on your upper thighs, as having the palms up prevents you from gripping and pushing down with your hands as you come to upright. Whilst sitting it also allows the weight of your arms to be taken by the legs, and encourages your shoulders to open and release away from each other.

I will now ask you to stand up. However I do not want you to do anything or get ready in any way. Instead, leave yourself alone and remain supported on the chair by your downward-pointing sitting bones. Give the directions for your neck, head and back, and direct your knees forward and away. You will also want to make sure that you are not stiffening your ankles, feet or toes in any way. Now I will ask you to stand. Once again inhibit.

Giving the verbal stimulus to move at least twice, but refusing to act on both occasions will often bring you to a place where you really do have an authentic choice about moving or not. If that is the case, perhaps now is time to stand. Keep your directions going and allow me to move you out of the chair with my hands (note there are different ways to accomplish this) without actively helping or hindering in any way. In particular you want to ensure that you do not directly activate, or push with, your legs. Instead, keep looking out, maintain the directions so that your head goes forward and up and your back goes back, while allowing your knees to release forward from the hip joints as you put them apart a little, while directing your ankles together. You will now be standing. You now have a template for carrying out sitting and standing by yourself.

Sitting and standing in everyday life

After your Alexander sessions it is time to put into practice what you have learned in these lessons. Will you always remember? No – at least not at first. But the key point to bear in mind when getting in and out of the chair, is that you want to prevent the pull of your head down on to the neck, which sets off most of the other distortions in your torso and limbs. That will involve pausing and giving the directions – although if everything is going well and you are

Sitting down

Do not respond to the stimulus to sit down, but instead look out and give your directions for your head, neck and back

Place your feet about hip-width apart, toes turned out slightly

Think of an upward release through your ankles, knees and hips

Come slightly up and back from the pivot point of your ankles

Allow your knees to release forwards gently and steadily from your hip joints and away from each other over the feet

Maintain the directions for the head, neck and back as you sit down – the trajectory will work itself out if you carry on looking out

As you touch the chair you will be inclined forward, so pause and order your spine to lengthen and your back to widen, think of your tailbone dropping, and then hinge your upper body back to upright

Standing up

Do not respond to the stimulus to stand up but do look out

Inhibit the idea that the movement out of the chair is led by your chin or chest, pulling the back in, or pulling the legs together. Instead give the directions for your primary control

Move toward the front of the chair if you are sitting at the back or in the middle

Ensure that your legs are drawn back slightly with your feet flat on the floor

Think of an upward release through your ankles, knees and hips

Allow yourself to come back a little from your hip joints, which will encourage your back to widen, while maintaining the directions for your primary control

Let your feely poised head (not the face) lead you out of the chair, direct your back to stay back and your knees to go forward from the hip joints, then put them away from each other, while directing your ankles together

Sitting and standing with one foot behind the other

You might also wish to experiment with Alexander's original method of sitting and standing, where one foot is placed behind the other. Learning another way of getting in and out of the chair ensures that the process of moving up and down in space, while maintaining internal length, provides you with another option to think in activity.

Stand with your feet in a fore-aft attitude, toes turned out slightly, with your back leg almost touching the chair. Look out. Now inhibit and give your directions in the correct sequence – neck, head, back as well as the appropriate messages for your legs and arms. Maintain the balance of your head on the neck and the lengthening and widening of the torso, and then allow your knees to move forward over the toes at the same time as your hip joints move backwards. You have now reached the chair with your sitting bones, and are leaning forward. Pause, give your directions, and then come to upright by rotating your upper body at the hip joints, without pulling back your head, lifting the chest, or pulling the legs together.

Standing up is the same sequence in reverse. Inhibit and direct before drawing back both feet ensuring that one foot is slightly under the seat of the chair (it does not matter if that contact is on the ball of the foot), let your head lead so that you are leaning forward from the hip joints while your spine continues to lengthen. You might also find it effective to add the order 'back to release up and back' to prevent pitching too far forward. Be careful not to tighten your ankles, knees or hips. When your body weight has transferred from your sitting bones to the platforms of your feet, and you are no longer in contact with the chair, direct your feet to release into the floor and slowly allow the backs of the knees and the fronts of the hip joints to open so that your legs straighten and you come to upright.

Many students of the Alexander Technique find this way of sitting down very practical as it typically prevents the collapse many people experience on reaching the chair. In standing up it also has an advantage in that the position of the feet provides some purchase – your head has less distance to travel forward when one foot is brought back. Of course, when you have stood up it also provides an excellent starting point for walking forward.

Moving in and out of the chair in this way is also useful if you are wearing a short skirt as the knees are not put apart so much as in the other version. This pattern of movement in and out of the chair is also beneficial for those recovering from hip, knee or back surgery.

maintaining lengthening of the stature, inhibition and direction are no longer separate but merge into one another as an on-going process or flow, two sides of the same coin, so to speak.

But let's assume, for the sake of argument, that you are not experiencing that benign state of flow. What to do? Well, you have plenty of opportunities throughout the course of the day when you sit and stand at work or leisure to inhibit and direct and to get a more efficient working of your primary control. That will be of enormous benefit to your health and well-being.

Everyday sitting

Many students erroneously believe that the type of 'active' sitting they perform in an Alexander lesson, in which lengthening back muscles provide support, is how they should expect to sit in everyday life, say, even when relaxing watching television. In fact how you sit in a lesson without using the back of a chair is primarily about how you move in and out of a chair. It's also the type of 'active' balanced sitting that's useful if you are playing the guitar, piano or violin, or perhaps when giving a talk or presentation.

For everyday purposes, say at work, it is probably best to use the support of your sitting bones and the back of a chair, which should be positioned as far under your desk or workstation as possible. In order to move yourself from the edge or middle to the back of the chair, it is important that you do not collapse, which will create a C-shaped curve in your spine and displace forward your sitting bones. Instead, without interfering with the balance of your head on your neck, and with one or both feet flat on the floor, place your arms behind your torso on to the flat of the chair, make loose fists with the front of your hands facing forward, and use the two largest knuckles of

> ### Active Sitting
>
> *Active sitting is relevant to a variety of activities including presentations, playing a musical instrument, or sitting on a stool*
>
> *Look out and be aware of space around you*
>
> *Think of your head releasing forwards and up, a lengthening from your tailbone up along your spine, and a widening of your torso*
>
> *Allow both feet to remain flat on the ground, your knees releasing forwards from your hip joints and away from each other*
>
> *Allow your upper body weight to be supported by your downward-pointing sitting bones*

Above Active sitting is relevant to a wide variety of situations

each hand for support. Without raising the shoulders lift your body so that your seat comes off the chair, and allow yourself to move backwards.

When you are once again sitting on your downward-pointing sitting bones, maintain your directions, especially the thought of the back widening and allow yourself to slowly hinge back from your hip joints so that your torso is reclining and supported against the back of the chair. When you want to come forward, pause, give your directions, and allow your knees to go slightly apart while directing your ankles together as you rotate your upper body from the hip joints to come back to the vertical. If you wish to get out of the chair, place your hands behind your torso, or if there is not space to the side take hold of the back of the chair and move yourself to the front using the minimum amount of effort.

Another effective way of moving forward and backward in the chair is to give the orders for the primary control, then support yourself with the first two knuckles of your hands and employ your body's spiral mechanism to good effect by walking on your sitting bones.

Sitting at leisure

If you are sitting in your leisure time, say, at home or in a cafe, rather than positioning yourself midway on the seat and slumping backwards, it is best to use the support of the back of the chair in the way just described. (If you need or like extra support for the lower back, you can position a small, firm cushion between you and the back of the chair.) However whilst sitting on a settee or a deep, wide chair, especially if you have short legs, feel free to assume a cross-legged, tailor-style attitude if you are able to do so without strain.

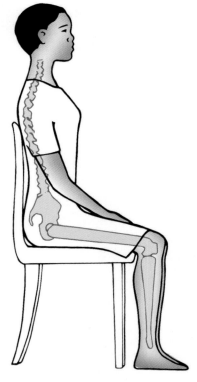

Above Using the back of a chair for support

The key point about the legs in sitting is to allow them to go forward from your hip joints and away from each other. It's important to emphasise that this order is not concerned with 'position' but with direction – that is, the lengthening of your leg muscles through your conscious orders. For example, you can sit with your upper body weight dropping through your sitting bones, with one leg supported by the opposite thigh, with or without the support of the back of the chair, or you can sit with the support of the back of a chair with your legs in front of you with ankles crossed with at least part of your feet on the ground. Both attitudes are compatible with the direction knees to go forward and away.

It's also worth pointing out that it is not a good idea, as many of us do, to sit with the feet off the ground and tucked underneath, or to cross the legs at the thighs. Although it's certainly possible, to sit in either attitude without compressing or tightening, the chances are that even if you start off reasonably well, it will not be too long before you will be pulling your head back and down as muscular contraction and twisting in your legs and torso gradually increases to keep you from falling forward.

If the chair or sofa you are sitting on has arm rests and you want to use them, simply allow the weight of your arms to release into the contact surface at the same time as you maintain freedom in the neck and allow the crown of your head to release upwards away from the open support of your sitting bones and feet. You can add on other directions, such as your shoulders releasing away from each other, as appropriate. Those directions will help to create or maintain a dynamic elasticity throughout your body when at rest.

Taking a break

Humans have evolved so far at least to move, not to remain stationary for any great length of time. But we have seen the ubiquitous chair and the sedentary nature of most people's work has changed that aspect of our lives,

Above Using the back of a sofa for support with ankles crossed is a nice way to sit

seemingly for ever. Many of us erroneously feel that we must sit for long periods of time in order to maintain momentum and complete our work. 'I can't stop otherwise I will lose my train of thought,' a 32-year-old student of the technique who is never far from her laptop told me recently. In reply, I pointed out that the longer she sat working at the keyboard, the more likely she would become fatigued and go into a C-shaped slump. Apart from the negative effects on the structure of the spine, scientists working in the fast-growing field of 'inactivity research' have recently discovered that sitting in a collapsed position for long periods has significant adverse effects on breathing, muscles, blood vessels, insulin sensitivity and metabolism. It also adversely affects the working of the eyes. Those factors, individually and collectively, have a huge impact on your ability to think clearly.

In general it is a very good idea to get out of the chair and take a break every 20-25 minutes or so and perform some light activity. For example, walking around for a few minutes and giving your directions will not only raise good (HDL) cholesterol levels and prevent your anti-gravity muscles atrophying, but also stimulate your breathing and provide extra energy for the work that you are doing. You might even try standing up to answer your phone. Those consciously

According to the World Health Organisation physical inactivity is the fourth leading risk factor for global mortality causing an estimated 3.2 million deaths annually. Recent research carried out in New South Wales found that in a group of 220,000 workers those who reported sitting for 11 hours or more each day had an increased mortality risk of 40 per cent over the next three years consistent across the sexes, age groups, and body mass index categories compared with those who sat for less than four hours. This was the case even with people of normal weight, who took the recommended 30 minutes of physical activity five times a week. 'When you are standing or walking, your leg muscles are constantly working which helps to clear blood glucose and blood fats from the blood stream,' says lead researcher Dr Hidde Van der Ploeg of the University of Sydney. 'If you are sitting, this is not happening because the muscles are not active.'

Another recent meta-analysis of nearly 800,000 people sampled in 18 previous studies, carried out by researchers from Leicester and Loughborough Universities, concluded that those who sat the most had a higher risk of diabetes, cardiovascular disease and kidney disease than those who sat the least. 'People convince themselves they are living a healthy lifestyle, doing their 30 minutes of exercise a day,' explained lead researcher Dr Emma Wilmot. 'But they need to think about the other 23.5 hours.'

performed interruptions in the working day might even help you to think creatively, rather than determinedly and inefficiently plodding on to complete your tasks.

Getting out of a slump

Of course there are times, such as in long meetings, where it is not always possible to get up to walk about. The danger of going into a slump is ever present, therefore. Not all is lost. As we saw earlier if you find yourself slumping you can use small movements such as allowing your torso to rotate forwards or backwards slowly from your hip joints, or use the knuckles of your hands to lift yourself up and move forwards or backwards in the chair. Alternatively, rotate your torso in small circles clockwise and counter clockwise keeping your sitting bones in contact with the chair, as you have been taught in a lesson. These activities, if properly performed, will help you to maintain an elastic tone throughout your musculature, and improve your general coordination. All of which is a very useful skill for life which leads us on to learn more about bending.

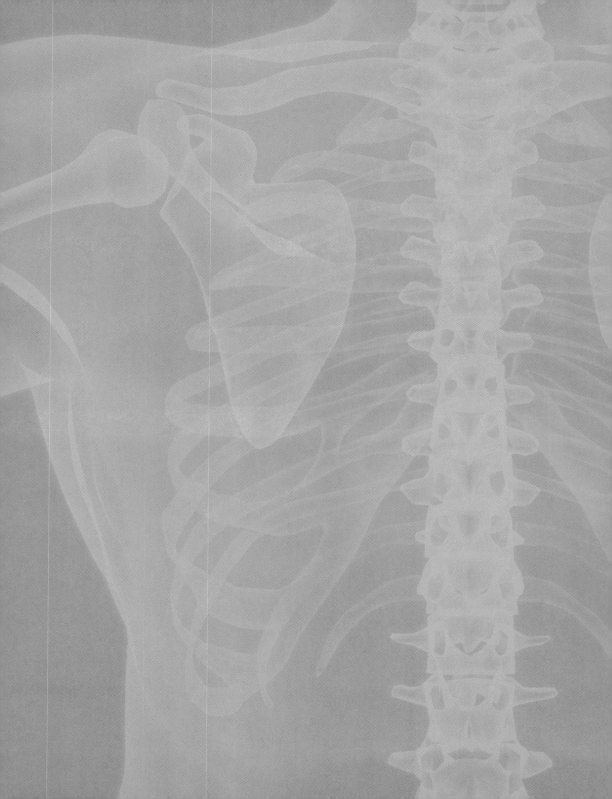

Chapter 7 – *Bending*

'The human machine certainly meets more differing conditions and performs work of greater diversity than any known mechanism. These functions are efficiently discharged when the body is in a state of poise. Visceral functions (such as those of digestion, circulation, respiration, and excretion) as well as physical activities must continue with a maximum of efficiency and the minimum interference with their rhythm whether the body is supine or prone, erect or bent, twisted or straight'

Raymond Dart

'A healthy back requires an appropriate balance between how much you use your back and how well your back functions. A normal, fit back needs to have a considerable degree of flexibility, strength, and endurance, as well as some degree of coordination and balance'

Daniel Lieberman

The movement cycle

In the last chapter we looked at sitting and standing. In reality the movement from upright to sitting on a chair and then back to upright can be viewed as part of a cycle in which keeping your internal length through activation of your body's anti-gravity musculature can always be taking place irrespective of where you are in space, or whether you are using your feet or something else, such as a chair or a horse, for support. This activity cycle necessarily takes in various forms of bending, a movement engineered by natural selection to take place as a reflex activity with minimum effort – except most of us do not experience it like that because of the inefficient way we carry it out.

This leads to a general, very noticeable reluctance to vary our height, which has some interesting consequences. It explains why, for example, premium-priced branded products in stores and supermarkets are positioned around eye level so that they are clearly visible and

easy to reach, while lower-value brands or generic items are relegated to the bottom shelves. The aim of shelf placement – what marketers call 'visual equity' – is to exert an influence on what we purchase. Although most of us would like to think we are far too sophisticated to be taken in by that kind of manipulative marketing, all the available evidence suggests that product placement works, both in retaining old customers and in attracting new ones. The reason is that time-poor reluctant-to-bend consumers have been conditioned to believe that what is around eye level is of higher quality than

Above Modern time-poor, reluctant-to-bend consumers favour products that are within easy reach

products positioned at a lower height. You can be sure that hunter-gatherers or nomadic pastoralists think very differently about the way in which they orient themselves to their material environment.

It's fairly common for many of us to make some sort of low groaning or moaning noise when we go from upright into bending or come from bending to upright. Sometimes this is associated with past or on-going experience of back pain, but not always. Emitting a vocal sound in such movements is neither useful nor normal. If you find yourself doing it, it is a sign that you are making unnecessary effort. Nevertheless these sounds do highlight something interesting. As nearly two-thirds of your weight is in your upper body you will appreciate that leaning forward or returning to upright are highly complex processes, and very easy to get wrong.

Squatting and non-squatting cultures

As we have seen in traditional cultures people routinely squat on their haunches or sit on the floor for a wide variety of purposes. By contrast, most of us do not have such a rich and complex relationship with the ground. In the home not only are there chairs, but a vast array of furniture and equipment is available there which diminishes the need to lower our height – think of tables, desks, beds, ovens, kitchen surfaces, shelves, cupboards, toilets, washbasins, remote controls and so on. A similar infrastructure in the workplace, entertainment and leisure spaces, in

Above Vietnamese woman squatting well

supermarkets and other retail outlets, further limits our range of movement.

As the objects which we touch, pick up and manipulate are routinely placed at around mid-height or above – nearer our heads than our feet, in other words – inevitably that means we routinely bend much less compared with those who live in societies which preserve squatting (and sitting on the floor) as customary behaviour, for example, when giving birth, caring for infants, going to the toilet, preparing food, or gathering together for group meals or religious functions.

It would be naive to assume that the ability to squat always has a benign outcome. A study of nearly 1900 Beijing men and women aged 60 or over who, as young adults, were used to performing a deep squat while using the toilet, cooking, eating, doing housework, washing clothes, talking to friends and family, and working found that the activity was a risk factor in developing arthritis of the knees, compared with a group of non-squatting white subjects from the Framingham area of Massachusetts. The research team at Boston University School of Medicine also discovered that the Beijing subjects, who spent three or more hours in a deep squat, had a far greater chance of developing the condition because of the sustained contact forces operating on the knee joints than those who squatted less frequently. However, an earlier study by the same research team found in a group of 1,506 elderly Beijing residents that pain and osteoarthritis in the hip joints was around 80—90 per cent less frequent than in white elderly populations in the US. Interestingly, the condition did not increase with age in the Chinese subjects.

Above Not using the ankles, knees and hips properly compresses the spine and distorts the back

Nonetheless we all need to bend forward from time to time. The key point here is that although the spine is inherently flexible the assumption most of us make that spinal pliability can be used instead of obtaining an upward release through our ankles, knees and hips, the major movable joints of the legs, is deeply flawed. As we saw in the last chapter, every time a decision to move is made, most of us go off-balance, or increase imbalance, by pulling our heads down on to our necks.

That same pattern of malcoordination is also evident in bending. The result is that when we pick things up from the floor, wash our hands, brush our teeth and chop vegetables in the kitchen, and so on, we end up pressing downward throughout the whole body, contracting both the flexor and extensor muscles of the trunk and limbs. For that reason it is hardly surprising that in people suffering from osteoporosis inefficient forward bending is associated with a high risk of spinal fractures.

Because bending is such an integral part of everyday life Alexander was keen to teach his students to perform the movement without distortion and compression by maintaining the integrity of the head, neck and back relationship, and using released ankle, knee and hip joints to lower their height. Influenced by some of his medical friends he initially referred to the movement as 'a position of mechanical advantage'. Later on the students on his training course dubbed it 'monkey' because someone performing it resembled (in their eyes) a non-human primate. The term was adopted by Alexander and remains the term of choice for Alexander Technique practitioners today.

Although most adults in our society will feel odd the first or second time they perform monkey, I should emphasise that there is nothing 'unnatural' about it – almost all of us would have been good at bending in this way when we were younger. Indeed, if you observe toddlers and small children with good coordination from any society (particularly before they have gone to school and developed a variety of poor biomechanical habits), you will notice that when they go to squat or pick up something from the floor, the head remains freely poised on the top of the spine, the back remains lengthened and widened, and the legs bend freely and easily. When they decide to come back to upright, they do so by straightening the legs without pulling the head back, pulling the back in or losing internal length.

In fact it is vitally important for your long-term health and well-being that you learn to bend without undue compression and strain. In short, you need to unlearn some of your bad habits, and find a way of carrying out the activity that you did with ease as a child. So let's look at what monkey entails in a bit more detail.

Monkey

In essence monkey is about achieving a better upright balance through direction and then lowering your height in space and bending without losing internal length – that is, although the leg joints are flexed and you are tilting forward from the hip joints, your overall internal length or height that might be traced between the soles of your feet and the crown of your head remains constant, a bit like a partial folding-up of a wooden tape measure.

Above A youngster squatting well

Two-stage monkey

When Alexander put someone in monkey he made sure that he had first obtained a release of the student's head on the neck triggering a lengthening of the spine and a widening of the back. There were then two more stages – bending the knees, followed by tilting forward from the hip joints. Alexander's methodology remains a good way to explore the movement. So I will ask you to look out and stand with your feet hip-width apart with your toes turned out slightly. Think of the front of your heels releasing into the contact surface of the floor and the rest of the foot, including your toes, releasing into length.

Now you want to achieve more internal length. You know that you cannot achieve this by muscular effort. Instead direct your head and heels away from each other, and then ask for an upward release through your ankles, knees and hips. Now allow yourself to come slightly up and back as a unit from the pivot points of your ankles at the same time as you release your knees forward and away over your feet. You can think of the movement as if the front and back of your torso are going down between a pair of imaginary vertical parallel lines, as you release upward from your tailbone along the length of your spine into your freely poised head. That will prevent you pushing your tummy forward and your upper back backwards. Throughout the activity, you also want to ensure that you keep breathing, so do not tighten the rib cage.

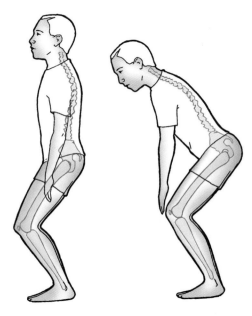

Above Monkey in two stages

You are now ready to come forward by rotating from your hip joints. It's very important to inhibit and direct at this juncture, because otherwise you will do it according to your habit and tighten. To ensure that you do not round the shoulders and collapse down the front of your body, a useful direction is to think of your shoulder blades staying flat on the upper back. Note this is another preventative order; you are not trying to do anything. You are simply aiming to stop distortion throughout your shoulder girdle as gravity comes more into play with the forward bend of your torso.

Although you should be able to perform the movement forward from the hips without any movement in your knees – they can remain still and continue to release while you maintain the contact of your heels with the floor – you may find it difficult at first. If that happens as you rotate forward from the hip joints, your head leading the torso into length, allow your knees to release a little more forward from your hip joints and tailbone, and away from each other. That will make it less likely that you will pull the legs into your body and stiffen. Allow your arms, which make up around eight per cent of your body weight, to hang out of your supportive back.

Once you are in monkey the directions that I will give to you are the same that Alexander used to give to his students: 'Neck free, head forward, knees forward, hips back – one against the other like a three-way stretch with the head just winning'. Once again remember not to fix your eyes in any position, but do look out and see something. Depending on how well you are going, I might also suggest that you now think of the direction along your back going in two directions – towards your head and towards your tailbone (an alternative is to think up the front and down the back of your spine).

It's important to understand that in monkey the relative positions of your head, legs and back do not matter – it is the relationship of parts to parts through direction that is important. In general terms you want to ensure that you keep your monkey free and mobile, especially at your ankles, knees and hips and maintain the contact of your heels with the ground, and a lengthening along your spine and a widening of your back. The elastic stretch or extension between different parts of your body which will be brought about is another good example of what Alexander referred to as antagonistic pulls.

How long you stay in monkey depends very much on how long you can keep the directions going. There is no point in staying in monkey once you begin to stiffen or experience any discomfort or achiness – in the Alexander Technique there is no virtue

> ### Directions for monkey
>
> *Look out*
>
> *Place your feet hip-width apart with the toes turned out slightly*
>
> *Give your directions for the primary control*
>
> *Think of an upward release through your ankles, knees and hips*
>
> *Maintain heel contact with the ground throughout the procedure*
>
> *Come slightly back from the vertical and allow your knees to release forward and away over your feet while maintaining your height*
>
> *Allow your head to lead the movement and pivot forward from the hip joints, while maintaining lengthening along the spine*
>
> *Order your shoulder blades to stay flat on the rib cage, and allow your arms to hang out of the back*
>
> *Give the directions: Neck free, head forward, knees forward and hips back – one against the other like a three-way stretch with the head just winning*

in suffering. In fact it is best to come up slowly well before any stiffening takes place, so the increase in muscle tone that has been generated is maintained as you move to upright. Let's now consider how that happens.

Coming out of monkey

Although Alexander taught going into monkey in a two-step sequence, coming out of monkey was performed in a single movement. So before you move, remember to pause, look out, give your directions for the primary control and then while still directing your knees forward from the hip joints and away from each other put your knees a little way apart from each other at the same time as you direct your ankles together and your feet into the ground. Then allow your knees and hips to straighten without bracing the legs, or lifting your chest and pulling your back in. That will allow you to come back to upright while maintaining internal length.

> ### Coming out of monkey
>
> *Look out*
>
> *Give your directions for the primary control*
>
> *Think of your knees going forward from the hip joints and away from each other over the toes*
>
> *Put your knees a little way apart, while directing the ankles together*
>
> *Think of your feet releasing into the ground*
>
> *Allow your legs to straighten*

A second way of coming out of monkey is to start the movement by releasing your knees forward a little, simultaneously letting your tailbone drop. That will have the effect of bringing your torso back to the vertical. At this point ensure that your body weight is dropping through your heels in such a way that the feet and the crown of your head are opposing one another. Now slowly allow your freely poised head to take you up in space as you direct your heels into the floor.

A third way of coming out of monkey is to maintain the directions for the primary control while allowing your right or left foot to peel off the floor and then take one or two steps forward, while thinking of the direction back 'up and back'. As you continue to move forward slowly release out of monkey to upright. You can also experiment with releasing out of monkey by walking backwards.

The one-stage monkey

Once you have practised and reached a good level of competence in the two-stage monkey, it is possible to perform the activity in a single movement – bending your knees forward flows smoothly into the release of the hips backward as you direct the head forward and up and your torso to lengthen and widen.

Now let's explore some other aspects of monkey.

Variations on monkey

Hip monkey

I first became aware of a different way to perform monkey when I visited the Indian Ocean island of Mauritius in the early 1980s. While walking I often observed small groups of middle-aged women working in the sugarcane fields. What was striking was the way in which *all* of them bent over by pivoting forwards from the hip joints, followed by a slight bend of the knees, without pulling their heads down on to their necks. They then moved steadily forwards,

Using the wall

Many students find that when performing monkey on their own it is all too easy to collapse and stiffen. One way around this problem is to use the support of a wall or door. Come back to the wall as you have already been taught (you can refer back to Chapter 4). Now direct your ankles to release so that the majority of your body weight drops through the heels into the floor, and only a small amount into the balls of your feet. Maintain your height as you allow your knees to release very slowly forward from your hip joints and away from each other, while your lengthening and widening back is directed back to the wall and your heels continue to pass your weight into the ground. At this stage you do not have to come down the wall – just allowing any bracing or stiffness in your knees to release is sufficient.

If you are successfully maintaining lengthening of the stature you can then bend your knees forward, and move one or more inches down the wall. Now allow yourself to incline forwards slightly from your hip joints with your tailbone maintaining a light contact with the wall. While giving the directions 'neck free, head forward, knees forward, hips back', you can then experiment with increasing the forward and backward tilt of your torso as well as allowing your knees to bend gently and steadily forward and away over the toes, being careful to maintain the open contact of your heels with the ground.

Additionally, as long as it does not trigger a collapse down the front of your body, you can choose to come forward from your ankles a little so that you are no longer in contact with the wall. That will mean that instead of your heels being the main point of contact with the ground you will need to find your own unsupported balance, with contact now being a tripod of support, your heels, and the pads of your feet behind the toes.

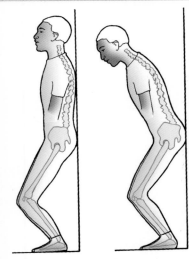

Above Using a wall to perform monkey

If your tail is still in touch with the wall, to come back to upright, inhibit and direct, and slowly allow yourself to pivot back to lean gently against the contact surface with a thought of an upward direction along your spine and a widening of your back. Direct your knees to go forward and apart as the legs straighten and you can return slowly to upright, being careful not to lose contact with your heels, or brace back your knees. If you are not touching the wall, come out of monkey in any of the ways you have been taught.

Monkey is not a static position, but rather one that achieves a release of the body's musculature through multiple directions that remain constant irrespective of what particular shape you happen to be in at any particular moment in time.

and occasionally sideways or backwards, using their hands for planting, weeding or rectifying furrows. With a number of legally guaranteed rest periods, the women did this for four or five hours from dawn, stopping before the sun got too high in the sky and it became unbearably hot. This work was – and still is – carried out only for a couple of weeks at a time. The result is that most women perform this type of bending for a maximum of 20 weeks a year, the rest of the time being filled with other tasks.

The incidence of musculoskeletal problems amongst Mauritian workers performing this type of labour has traditionally been low because of the limited periods they have to work. That fits very well with what is already known about cross-cultural patterns of back pain and injuries. Agricultural workers who perform arduous repetitive tasks for many hours day in, day out, and, at the other end of the spectrum, office workers who remain immobile for much of the day, are susceptible to a variety of musculoskeletal problems. The lesson is that whatever we do for a living we need to learn to use our bodies in a well-coordinated way, and, if it is socially or financially possible, limit the time we spend on a particular task, in order to maintain flexibility and strength.

In a pamphlet published by Alexander in 1910 entitled **Supplement to Re-Education of the Kinaesthetic Systems Concerned with the Development of Robust Physical Well-Being**, *under the heading 'Door Exercise', a very similar way of bending to that employed by the agricultural workers I had observed in Mauritius is described. You can read the full account in Alexander's edited* **Articles and Lectures**. *In the section that is relevant to bending, Alexander instructs the student to stand between 6 to 12 inches from a door and then allow the hips to move backwards so that the body is supported (by the buttocks and the platforms of the feet) at an angle of around 25 to 30 degrees. According to Alexander in carrying this out most people will stiffen the legs, whereas he suggests 'all that is necessary is that the pupil shall, as it were, cut off the energy which causes the firm position at the hip joints and other parts, and by ordering or desiring the relaxation of the parts concerned so that the hinge-like movement of the hips takes place, and the teacher with his hands placed upon the pupil causes his … body to move in the right direction.'*

Above The use of positions of mechanical advantage by workers in rice fields in India

You can observe a similarly efficient way of bending to that employed by Mauritian and agricultural workers in other parts of the world in some sports. For example, well-coordinated tennis players who are waiting to receive the ball from an opponent will allow the upper body to rotate forward from the hip joints, which in turn will trigger a reflex bending of the knees. Martina Hingis, winner of five Grand Slam singles titles, employs this method of going into monkey extremely well.

So let's work out how to perform this variation on monkey. What you learn about the process of bending in this way can then be employed when you need to pick something off the floor, play tennis or golf, or with numerous everyday tasks.

Stand with your feet about hip-width apart – more if you want – and the toes turned out slightly. Inhibit and give your directions.

Above Swiss tennis champion Martina Hingis releases into a forward lean from her hip joints, her eyes maintaining forward vision without creating neck tension

Allow your hip joints to release backwards as your head-led torso releases and tilts forward, but inhibit the reflex bending of your knees to keep the legs straight but not stiff. That will promote a good heel contact, especially if you direct your toes into length, so that your feet are opening into the floor. Maintain the heel contact and forward lean from the hip joints, and then gently and slowly allow your legs to bend forward, keeping the pelvis as an integral part of the torso. If you want you can then walk forwards or backwards before slowly coming to upright.

Many students like this way of performing monkey, as it helps to prevent a collapse in the torso and pulling the head back. It also provides an interesting variation on a theme – another way of looking at the challenge of bending and then coming back to upright, without shortening the stature.

Placing hands on a table in monkey

In the next chapter we explore in more detail how to use your arms and hands in everyday life but here I wish to draw your attention to how they can be used for support and to generate more elasticity in the body's musculature.

Stand near a table or work surface – if you are positioned too far back the tendency is to overreach with your hands and pitch too far forward – your feet hip-width apart and the toes turned out slightly. Allow yourself to go into monkey without contracting.

Once you are in the monkey, keep your wrists free, direct and then open your hands towards the floor in such a way that the fingers, thumbs and musculature of the arms lengthen. Allow time for this to happen as most of us have arms and hands that are unduly contracted. Be careful, however, not to interfere with the balance of your shoulders. Now with fingers leading allow one of your hands to make a light contact with the table, heel touching first and with your fingers slightly spread. Your hand will not be flat but will have a small arch. The process can then be repeated with your other arm. Your hands should be near your body, about shoulder-width apart.

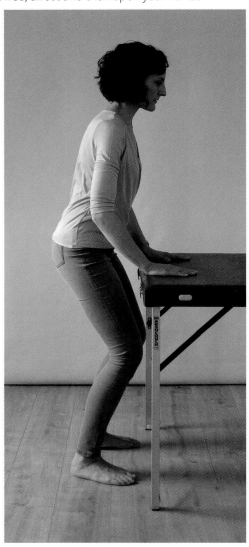

The contact with your hands and feet, especially the heels of both, means that you are now effectively 'four-footed'. Go through the directions for monkey – neck free, head forward, knees forward and hips back. You can also think of widening across the base of your back. You now have an opportunity to think creatively. Direct your upper arms to rotate outwards and the forearms to rotate inwards at the same time as you direct your shoulders to release apart and away from each other. Those preventative directions will keep your arms and shoulder girdle connected down and back into your back. Now, without doing anything, add on a direction for your hands to release into the

Above Placing the hands on a firm surface enables us to become 'four-footed'

Placing the hands on the table

Look out

Go into monkey

Allow your fingers to lead the arms and make a free and open contact with the table about shoulder-width apart

Give your directions for the head, neck, back and knees

Direct your upper arms to rotate outwards and the forearms to rotate inwards at the same time as you direct your shoulders to release apart and away from each other

Think of your hands releasing into the table and your feet into the floor

Add on the direction for your back (or spine) to release 'up and back'

table and your feet to release into the ground. The resultant four-footed support will allow you to become a sprung weight on the surface of the table and you will be releasing up off a pair of lively and open hands. You can also experiment with putting the knuckles or back of your hands on the table for support.

Being four-footed facilitates a further direction – ordering the back (or spine) up and back. This preventative direction is also relevant to any bending movement that you perform as it helps to maintain or generate lengthening and widening in your torso.

Squatting

Squatting is an activity that most of us should be well able to do – at least to some extent. In the short film of Alexander made in 1949 and 1950 there is a sequence where he demonstrates squatting and rising. What stands out is the ease with which the down-up movement is performed. Alexander had incredibly springy, elastic legs, which is all the more remarkable considering that he was around 80 years of age. If you have not already done so, you should definitely view this film.

The evolutionary significance of squatting

In addition to being tree-dwelling, our tailless quadrupedal ancestors in east Africa also spent a considerable amount of time on the ground looking for foods such edible plants, seeds and grubs. The problem was that these ape-like creatures could only use one limb to pick up such items as the other three had to be employed for support. According to zoologist and evolutionary biologist Jonathan Kingdon this led to a long series of small, adaptive changes resulting in these ape-like creatures using their hind legs to perform a resting squat (feet flat on the floor, buttocks resting on the calves), and employing their long forelimbs to forage and feed. Occasionally they would also assume a more upright stance and use the ability to swivel their heads and trunks (developed while their fingers combed the soil) to take a look around. This adaptation likely provided such early hominins with a better and more plentiful diet leading over time to habitual erect bipedalism and greater reproductive success. This might explain why modern humans possess a vertically short pelvis, a pronounced curvature in a long lumbar spine, a twisty waist, a forwardly-placed balance point where the head sits on the neck, robust heels, and powerful leg and torso muscles.

Squatting obviously involves lowering your height more than that of a conventional monkey. For that reason you will require a relatively wide base, with the toes well turned out. I will provide you with the necessary support so that you do not tighten and lose stature as you move. Inhibit and direct, and whilst maintaining your heel contact allow your knees to release forwards and away so that your descent is as vertical as possible. At the point when vertical descent is no longer an option, I will guide your torso forward from your hip joints. Your arms will be hanging out of your lengthening and widening back.

If you are insufficiently flexible you can bend as far as you can without causing strain and compression. Then return to upright. Over time, working in this way you should find that you will be able to gradually increase the amount of bending. But the important word here is gradually. Remember the Alexander Technique is process–oriented rather than goal-oriented. There should be no attempt to force yourself to conform to what you imagine you should be able to do, or what you have seen someone else do.

Performing a squat puts a significant demand on the system for those who are unfamiliar with it. For that reason you should not attempt to force yourself to stay in a squat longer than you are able. The movement should remain free and flexible at all times. If you experience any sort of strain – in this instance your kinaesthetic sense will be very reliable – it is a signal that you are overdoing it. Don't ignore it!

Above A blind Afghan man squatting

Squatting

Look out

Assume a relatively wide base with your toes turned out

Maintain contact with your heels on the floor at all times

Give your directions for the primary control

Order an upward release through your ankles, knees and hips

Allow your knees to release forwards and away over your feet while your torso remains vertical

Allow your head to lead the torso into length as you rotate forward from your hip joints

Allow your arms to hang out of your lengthening and widening back

Coming up out of the squat is very similar to how you come up out of monkey. Let your head release forward and up, leading the spine into length, order your knees forward and away, and then put the knees apart, while directing your ankles together and your heels down, both before you come up and as you are coming up.

Right A man demonstrating the art of climbing a coconut tree in Kerala, India

Squatting using a support

If you are a beginner, especially if there is a problem with flexibility, you can squat using a post at the base of the staircase, or something similar. Pause and give your directions for the primary control, and then stand about an arm's length from the post in a wide stance with your feet well turned out. Let your lengthening fingers lead and wrap your open hands around the post – the sort of grip you might have seen employed by someone climbing a coconut tree – slightly above belly button height. Direct your hands to release towards each other as the shoulders release away from each other, and your feet release into the floor. Now, think of an upward release from your ankles through your knees and hips, and lean up and back as a unit from your ankle joints so that your arms straighten but are not held fixed or rigid.

Allow your knees to bend forward and away over your toes while your back stays back. If you can go down all the way to the floor without strain while keeping your internal length, and, most importantly, your heels on the floor, that's fine. But if you cannot it is important to recognise your limitations. In that case, you should stop moving immediately you pick up a signal that you are tightening your muscles, losing the heel contact with the floor, or fixing your rib cage.

Wherever you have ended up, you now have the challenge of returning to upright without contracting. So let your head lead, and then slowly put your knees further apart while you direct your ankle together and your feet, especially the heels, into the floor before you begin the movement, and as you go through it. It's also important not to pull yourself forward but to maintain an up and back trajectory while keeping your arms straight. You are now upright, but leaning backwards from the post. Pivot forward slowly from your ankle joints so that you are vertical and in balance, the crown of your head releasing skywards, and your feet opening into the ground.

If you find that you cannot squat very far, you might benefit from placing some paperback books under your heels. As your leg muscles, especially the hamstrings, become accustomed to working at an increased length you can reduce the amount of support. Over time, as long as you inhibit and direct, it should be possible for you to go into a lower squat. However, if for some structural or other reason you cannot increase the depth of bending, it is still a useful activity as it will help you maintain muscular elasticity.

Squatting and sitting

Squatting is also relevant to sitting. Alexander used to point out to his students that a good way to overcome our habitual response to the chair was to pretend it was not there, and organise yourself as if you were going into a deep squat. It's good advice. If you do not try to put your sitting bones on the chair, but instead allow your knees to move steadily forward, while maintaining the upward thought along the spine towards your freely-poised head, you are lowering your height without losing internal length. On reaching the chair you will be leaning forward from your hip joints. Allow yourself to be supported by your sitting bones and heels. Then, inhibit, direct and hinge your torso back to upright.

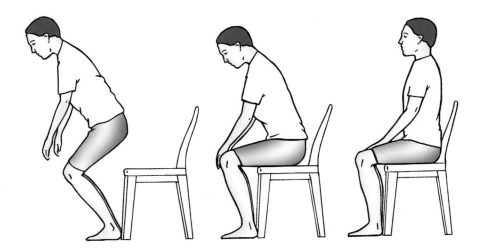

Above You can use a squat to lower your height and so indirectly sit on a chair

Bending and lifting

It's vitally important for you to carry out bending efficiently if it coincides with lifting something and moving it somewhere else. Many people create a significant amount of unnecessary tension in their bodies by stiffening the neck and bracing the torso, arms and legs in anticipation of picking up not only relatively heavy objects, such as a bag of cement or a dining chair, but also lighter items, such as a paperback book, mobile device or a cup of tea. If lifting and carrying heavy or even light loads is not performed well it will lead to a repeated experience of inappropriate muscle contraction, together with lots of breath-holding. Instead of the weight that is being lifted or carried being allowed to pass through your body into the support of the floor, it will be held or fixated at some juncture – perhaps in your arms and hands, shoulders, lower back, or the hips, knees and ankles – with possibly long-lasting injurious results. Once again this alerts us to the fact that the two separate acts of bending and the use of the arms and hands are often performed simultaneously. So how we use our upper limbs is where we go to next.

Above It's all too easy to pull in the back while moving a bulky or heavy object badly

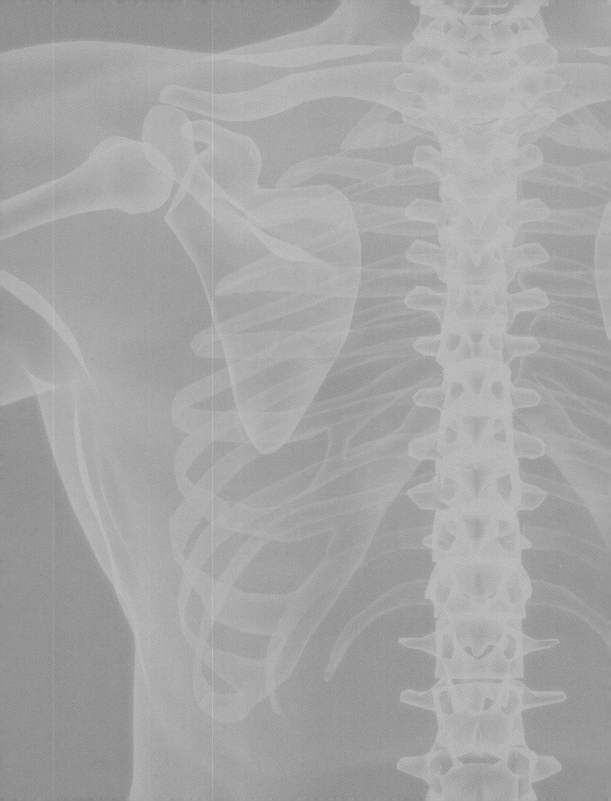

Chapter 8 – *Using shoulders, arms and hands*

'Man could not have obtained his present dominant position in the world without the use of his hands, which are so admirably adapted to act in obedience to his will'

Charles Darwin

The shoulder girdle, arms and hands

Being able to sit, squat or stand upright because of the body's extremely powerful hip and back musculature allows us to use our hands in ways unique among animals. The wide-ranging human ability to reach, grasp and manipulate a wide variety of objects – from peeling an apple, playing a guitar, moulding clay, text messaging to using chopsticks – is testament to an extraordinarily elastic musculoskeletal structure and the central nervous system that controls it.

Our capacity to handle objects at a range of angles is built partly upon flexibility and mobility in the shoulder girdle, a structure suspended over the rib cage and partly on our arms and hands. Without going into too much anatomical detail your collarbones (clavicles) are attached to the breastbone (sternum) at the front and to the triangular-shaped shoulder blades (scapulae) at the outer extremities of the shoulders. To appreciate just how flexible that structure is it is worth noting that the only bony connection between your shoulder girdle and the main skeleton is where your collar bones meet your breastbone.

Your arms are best thought of as appendages that are suspended from the central support of the bony spine and release outwards from your shoulder blades and other muscles in your back. Initially employed by infants lying in supine and prone and later in our culture used to crawl on all fours at around six months, the arms also play a key role in maintaining balance whilst walking with or without support at ten months and then from two years of age to run on two legs.

Around your first birthday you also develop the ability to point with an extended index finger to get and direct the attention of adults and children nearby to an object you find interesting – a hovering bumblebee, a slow-moving cat or a fast-moving airplane, for example. In turn that leads you to find the actual process of catching other people's attention intrinsically rewarding since you have learned that your gesture can initiate shared body-mind experiences. It's evident that purposeful or declarative finger-pointing, which triggers extension or lengthening of the arm, is something for which we are peculiarly

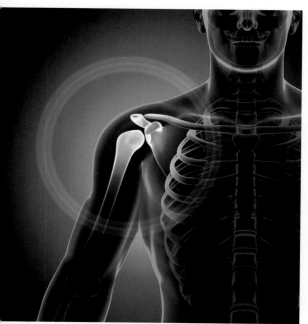

Above Illustration of shoulder girdle

well-adapted. It's a behaviour found in all cultures (though people in different cultures also learn to point with other fingers, chins, elbows and feet). Some developmental psychologists and palaeoanthropologists go further and claim that directed finger-pointing is a uniquely human gesture as no great ape living in the wild has ever been observed to use it. This ability is certainly used to good effect in the Alexander Technique.

Above A toddler pointing with his index finger

The capacity of your shoulder girdle to support the working of your arms and hands, including the fingers, to extend, flex and rotate is remarkable, especially when compared with that of your pelvic girdle and legs (you cannot scratch your back with your toes, for example). Your thumb is particularly important; just try lifting a glass with one hand without using it. The only way of accomplishing this is to use a scissor-like movement with two or more fingers. Awkward and doable, but the manoeuvre is more difficult and often messy, especially if liquid is involved. We have thumbs and it is best to use them.

Bonobos and chimpanzees with their long, strong and curved fingers and short, weak and opposable thumbs, are highly efficient at using a 'hook grip' of four fingers to climb, hang and swing from branch to branch in the treetops, or using the knuckles of the hands to walk (and run) on the ground for miles, activities which we are unable to emulate. Chimpanzees also use their hands to manipulate tools such as a stone hammer to crack open nuts, a leaf to drink water, or a small twig held between the sides of the thumb and index finger to fish for termites. There's little doubt they are some of the most amazing and intelligent creatures on the planet. But because of their anatomy chimps and other apes handle objects differently from us. Our ability to position the pads of our long, muscular and mobile thumbs in full opposition to the broad tips of our other relatively short, straight fingers allows us to grip, pinch or squeeze objects firmly and with great precision. This sets us apart, at least in this extent, from our closest living relatives.

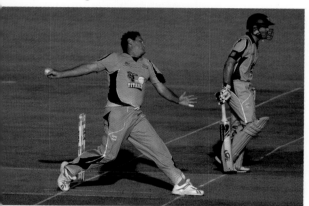

Above A cricketer ready to bowl

Some primates such as bonobos, chimpanzees, Barbary and Japanese macaques can throw sticks, rocks and other objects, but it is only humans who can throw missiles overarm with speed, force *and* great accuracy by virtue of more forward-facing, flexible shoulder joints that allow energy storage in stretched ligaments and tendons, rotation of the arm and pelvis, and flexible wrists and fingers. We also have powerful legs and resilient feet, and brains capable of great conceptual and spatial complexity. For example, you can see that combination of attributes when hunter-gatherers throw spears at prey, or cricketers perform pace or even spin bowling.

Indeed our talent for taking part in and interpreting one-handed throwing, especially in terms of calculating direction and distance, has led some evolutionary biologists and neuroscientists to claim that the initial development of this skill amongst early hominins was not, as Darwin and others have claimed, related to hunting with rocks or other missiles (an expertise which emerged some time later), but with self-expression and social play. But it is evident that throughout the course of human evolution throwing for whatever reason has led to an increase in the size of our brains and brought about changes in structure and functioning. These transformations are associated with a range of capacities such as manual dexterity and technological wizardry, language and speech, music and cooperative relationships, not just with kin but with strangers as well. One-handed throwing may have also been one of the factors that contributed to selection for a habitually upright stance and handedness.

Arms, hands and emotional expression

The examples of intentional finger-pointing and one-handed throwing demonstrate that the use of the hands and arms is not solely about grasping and manipulating objects. We are, after all, social animals who communicate with one another. Moving, or not moving, the arms and hands and other parts of the body, especially the face and eyes, with or without vocal sounds, are used by people of all cultures to indicate, or disguise, thoughts, feelings and intentions. As with any form of behaviour, gesture is a complex blend of physical and cultural skills directed towards communication and will vary from one society to another and between groups within a particular society. It's also dependent on social context. In my culture arm movements will be different when singing and dancing in time with the music at a pop concert, than while singing hymns at a funeral.

Pianists

Lang Lang

The arms and hands, as well as other parts of the body, also play a key role in both communication and expression in the performing arts. Let's take musician Lang Lang as an example. There is a technical aspect to the way the Chinese-born pianist uses his fingers on the keyboard, but there's an expressive aspect as well. At times he throws his arms in the air and rocks on his stool while at the keyboard. That, along with a penchant for loud jackets and spiky hair, goes some way to account for the widespread perception among his fans that Lang Lang is unique in managing to combine dazzling classical technique with rock star showmanship.

It's a pity though that in order to express the meaning of the music to his audience, Lang Lang often shortens in stature – specifically he leans back and creates a C-shaped torso. There's no doubt that this habit interferes with the sound he produces. Perhaps not surprisingly some music critics have accused Lang Lang of being 'uneven' and 'heavy-handed'.

At times Lang Lang allows the back of the hand to lead his arm up and away from the keyboard so that it is directly in front of him, all the while maintaining a free wrist. The arm hangs in the air for a few seconds, taking a rest, as it were. Whatever the origins of this practice – does it come from classical technique, rock star showmanship, or a combination of the two? – it generates at least *some* lengthening and freedom in the fingers, arm and shoulder musculature. Whether he realises it or not this movement is probably Lang Lang's saving grace.

Yet rather than rely on a specific muscular release in the arms and shoulders it would be much better for Lang Lang to achieve a coordinated release throughout his body. If you play a keyboard I'm sure you are wondering how that can be achieved. There are a few general points to make. Firstly, pay attention to how you move down in space to sit on the stool, as that will have a significant impact on the efficiency of the movement of your hands and feet once you are seated (refer back to Chapter 6). Secondly, maintain a good contact with your sitting bones, the crown of your head releasing in the opposite direction, so that support from the pelvis connects with the elasticity of your shoulders, arms and hands. Thirdly, it is always a good idea to observe those who play an instrument with excellent coordination. You can then try to work out what they are doing and, very importantly, what they are not doing. From that perspective the late Artur Rubinstein provides a brilliant example.

Above Lang Lang (left) and Artur Rubenstein (right) approach playing the piano in very different ways

Artur Rubinstein

Widely acclaimed as one of the greatest classical pianists of the 20th century, Rubinstein certainly used his body to express his feelings as he played. Unlike Lang Lang, however, the Polish-born maestro did not lose height when he moved. Although nowhere near as animated as Lang Lang, Rubinstein was certainly not stiff, and as well as moving forwards and backwards, he also had a habit of gently rocking from side to side, maintaining a good connection between the head, neck and back and arms, all the time using his eyes to good effect. 'I like to look up over the piano so I can listen and follow the lines of the piece,' he explained. 'Looking at your fingers for accuracy is too confusing. I'd rather miss a few notes than play by phrase instead of as a whole.'

Even in his late 80s Rubinstein maintained excellent general coordination whether he was sitting still, or moving forwards, backwards or sideways. As a consequence the great maestro's fingers and hands always floated – perhaps danced would be a better word – over the keyboard doing what they had to do, but no more. No music critic ever accused Rubinstein of bashing the piano keys, or thought of bestowing on him the nickname 'Bang Bang' as with Lang Lang.

Dancing

Irish dancing

A further example of the important role of arms and hands in performance is provided by recent changes in Irish dancing. In the traditional dance form the arms are kept close to the sides often with the hands made into loose fists, while quick and intricate footwork, including leaps and jumps, is performed. The contrast between passive arms and active legs is of central significance and meaning.

Above Riverdance

Irish dancing has evolved considerably over the last few decades. *Riverdance*, choreographed by the Irish-Americans Michael Flatley and Jean Butler, became a worldwide hit in the mid-1990s, and was quickly followed by a number of sequels, including Flatley's *Lord of the Dance* and Butler's *Dancing on Dangerous Ground*. In the new form the dancers are no longer obliged to keep their arms by their sides, but at times can place their hands on their waists, above the heads and even use them to lift their fellow dancers in to the air.

That transformation, as Butler later explained, was extremely rewarding to those involved as 'choreographically and stylistically we were extending the natural line of the Irish Dancing "body". We were also working within the context of interpreting a narrative, which opened up the idea of physical characterization.' Importantly, that meant that the new style could be used in musical theatre, rather than the national and international dance competitions normally associated with Irish dancing.

So do all Irish dancers move with freedom and grace? Obviously not. As with any expressive art form some people have a better working of the primary control, muscular elasticity, spatial awareness and rhythm than others. Nevertheless it is certainly true that without a good degree of freedom in the shoulder girdle, arms and hands, the incredibly high leaps in both traditional and modern Irish dance that some performers achieve would be impossible.

Hip-hop

The importance of maintaining muscular elasticity in the torso and limbs also holds for other dance styles, whether jazz, salsa, tap or ballroom. It's particularly relevant for forms such as body popping, locking and electric boogaloo, 'funk styles' which emerged on the streets on America's West Coast in the 1960s and 70s that later fused with others, including breaking, that developed around the same time on the East Coast. This new dance hybrid spread globally very quickly through television and film and has had an enormous impact on popular culture. In the early 1980s I encountered (and wrote about) a group of working-class teenagers of diverse ethnicities who regularly gathered after school and at weekends in a car park behind the London Hospital in Whitechapel to try out various moves such as the electric wave, the windmill and back spinning. It was fascinating to observe the body being put to such uses, in particular the way differences in general coordination between those involved affected both

Above Hip-hop has become a global phenomenon

learning and performance though from an anatomical perspective I remain unconvinced about the wisdom of spinning at speed on one's head!

Nowadays so-called hip-hop or urban dance is no longer confined to the streets but has become mainstream, routinely performed in dance studios, pop concerts and musical theatre. Nonetheless it remains a relatively 'open' dance style. Many artists within this genre continue to use a wide variety of improvised, free-form hand, arm and shoulder movements as well as mime, often to great dramatic effect.

If you are a novice, or an average hip-hop dancer, keen to improve your artistry and technique, let me repeat the general point made earlier about learning through observation of highly-skilled performers. In this instance you would do well to study a dancer such as Los Angeles-born street dancer turned choreographer and musician Jeffrey Daniel, the man who taught Michael Jackson how to 'backslide' or 'moonwalk', and a hero to many of my young East End friends. Daniel's movement is extraordinary. Even though he is now approaching his seventh decade he maintains an extraordinary flexibility over his limbs based on a wonderful control over his head, neck and back relationship. In performance terms there is little to differentiate his older self from his younger one. If you get the opportunity to attend one of Daniel's dance workshops you should observe him closely and then ask him how he is able to maintain flexibility *and* strength in movement.

Above Los Angeles-born urban dancer Jeffrey Daniel

Alexander Technique and the performing arts

But what can the Alexander Technique teach you if you already exhibit good coordination in your chosen performing art? For a start, it will be in your interests to find out exactly what you are conscious of and what you are not. If you already have good awareness over your head, neck and back, there may not be much to teach you. On the other hand it is entirely possible that your good coordination in performance does not permeate routine, everyday activities such as getting in and out of the chair, or picking up a kettle. You can be sure that over time misuse in these other activities will affect your general movement.

On the other hand if you are someone who possesses good coordination but who is not consciously aware of how movement takes place you will gain a huge advantage in becoming more aware of your skill-set. For example, in your favoured genre in dance that can be a great help because it will help you explore how to move 'elegantly and cleanly in space before attempting something too advanced as this may foster bad habits', as Jean Butler neatly puts it. In Alexander Technique terms that involves consciously working out how to keep your head poised, while using fully the double spiral musculature around the central supporting axis of the spine, and moving through space rhythmically using your arms and legs efficiently and expressively. As a bonus, improving your kinaesthetic sense will also offer protection from various forms of repetitive strain injuries. One way to achieve those benefits is to learn to use your arms and hands efficiently in taking hold of the top rail of a chair.

Hands over the back of a chair

Tired arms

Like all actors, Alexander took a keen interest in the use of the hands and arms, precisely because of their expressive or signalling function in human communication both on the stage, and in other types of performance, including the performance of everyday life.

Alexander had a pressing need to develop fine control over his upper limbs, because after he began full-time teaching of his technique in Australia he found that by the evening he was unable to straighten his arms because of tension. As with the influence on vocalisation of what he was doing with his legs and feet, Alexander came to appreciate more fully that there is a reciprocal relationship between the arms and hands, and the head, neck and back.

Given his nature, he began looking for a solution to his problem. He became particularly intrigued by a procedure brought to his attention by one of his male students who had learnt that a good way to achieve chest expansion was to take hold of the back rail of a chair, employing what is now termed a 'power grip' (using a flexed palm, fingers and thumb), and exert a horizontal pulling action.

Initially through observation but then by performing the procedure himself, Alexander realised that although the exercise could undoubtedly bulk up the chest musculature, it also narrowed rather than expanded the rib cage (a physiological pattern also evident in many of today's bodybuilders and gym enthusiasts). Specifically, he realised that the way most people did it using a power grip not only caused excess tension in the arms and hands, but also resulted in stiffening the neck, pulling the head back, raising the chest, pulling the back in, and tightening the legs and feet. Alexander then worked out that there was a way to carry out the activity employing a particular type of 'precision grip', using the pad of the thumb and extended fingers flexed from the first joint of the hand, with the minimum of effort that would open and tone the musculature of the torso. He also realised that his highly innovative way of performing the procedure not only led to greater efficiency in the way the arms and hands are used but also to an improved working of the respiratory system. That insight can be applied to a great variety of other activities.

As we have already noted Alexander's hands over the back of a chair procedure evolved over time. But throughout his teaching career, Alexander regarded the activity as extremely important. In general Alexander reserved teaching hands over the back of the chair for those with some experience of the technique as he did not want people to view it as a conventional exercise. The procedure was taught in both sitting and standing.

Hands over the back of a chair in standing

You will need a reasonably high-backed chair with a relatively straight, flat top rail. In standing it is important you do not position yourself too near the chair in front in order to avoid being cramped. You are going to bend, so your feet will be hip-width apart, with the toes turned out slightly. Inhibit, give your orders and then release into a shallow monkey.

In performing hands over the back of a chair the angle of your torso in monkey can vary and it is worthwhile exploring that range as that way you will learn how to bend and use your arms and hands in a wide range of activities, including those required in dance, dramatic or musical performance.

Once you are in monkey, the directions are 'Neck free, head forward and up, back to lengthen and widen, knees to go forward and away; head forward, knees forward, hips back.' You might also find it useful to add on the order 'back (or spine) to release up and back'. Remember that those orders are to be given one after another and subsequently all at the same time.

You now want to place your hands on the rail of the chair. Before making any movement bear in mind that you will tend to favour one hand over the other. That pattern of handedness, as we have seen, reflects in large part the asymmetrical structure and functioning of your brain. The chances are you will select your right hand to make the first movement along with 90 per cent of the rest of the population. But whatever your bias you will want to play around with choosing which of your hands moves first.

There are many good ways to place your hands on the rail of the chair. Here are two. Both involve inhibiting and giving the orders for the primary control before directing and letting your fingers and thumbs lengthen so that the hands open before moving or as you move your arms. In the first method, allow your fingertips to lead the movement of one arm so that it is pointing forward directly in front of you just below shoulder height. Keep in mind that your shoulder girdle operates as part of your back and that your arm pivots or releases forward from its furthest extremity. Now slowly bend your extended fingers at the first joint of your hand to form a beak-like shape.

Next, take hold of the top rail of the chair gently but firmly, with your wrist curved slightly inwards counterbalanced by your elbow curved slightly outwards. Your fingers and thumb need to be both straight *(but not stiff)* and vertical, pointing downwards, preferably near the top of the chair rail. Be careful also not to press your fingers together as that only creates tension. The pad of your thumb can be placed opposite any of the fingers. However, you will typically find that a grip opposite your second finger is optimal as it promotes a release initially in your armpit and then outward through the arms and shoulder girdle. That, in turn, allows the important anti-gravity musculature of your back to work and provides support for your head and neck, and the limbs. Repeat the process for your other arm.

Above Performing hands over the back of a chair

The second way of placing your hands involves starting the movement from the elbow of one arm, which you first direct away from your chest wall and then move forward before it tracks in as if it was going round a large beach ball. Place your extended, downward-pointing fingers and thumb, once again with your wrist curved slightly inwards and your elbow outwards, on the rail of the chair. Repeat the process for your other arm.

Different Alexander traditions have evolved different ways of positioning the hands on the chair rail. But the way I am describing here is the one Alexander himself taught towards the end of his life. In this 'classic' method whichever way you decide to place your hands, it is important not to create a 'break' at the wrists. Your hands should be a continuation of your arms, without the wrists bending upwards or downwards. You also want to ensure that your hands are several inches or more apart on the rail of the chair.

Once both hands are in place on the rail of the chair remember to look out while monitoring the working of your head, neck and back to make sure that you are not stiffening your knees, ankles, or toes, or collapsing or pulling down the front of your torso. At this point

Above Placing hands over the back of a chair requires vertical and straight fingers and thumbs

think of your shoulders releasing away from each other and then allow that release to flow down the backs of your arms to the elbows, along the forearms and out to the wrists, hands and fingers. As your muscles relax and release into length the quality of your hand grip will improve without you having to 'do' anything. Then allow your arms to slowly move up and down a little while maintaining the gentle but firm grip of straight fingers and thumbs on the chair and the direction of your wrists to curve inward and your elbows outwards. The ease and efficiency of that flapping action will reveal whether or not you are making any unnecessary tension in your arms and shoulders.

Now add on to the other directions a thought of your elbows releasing outwards and slightly downwards while your fingers and thumbs remain anchored to the rail of the chair. That will trigger a gentle forearm pull to your elbow. Think of a further order to widen the upper part of your arms – a good reference point being the inside of the upper part of each upper arm, just below the arm pit – away from the chest wall in such a way that your torso is supported by your arms. Now don't do anything; instead just *think* of lifting and stretching apart the rail of the chair as if it was a piece of elastic, whilst your feet continue to release into the floor.

Hands over the back of a chair in standing

Look out, inhibit and direct, and release into a shallow monkey

Direct your neck to be free, your head to go forward and up, and your back to lengthen and widen

Throughout the procedure ensure that you do not stiffen your knees, ankles or feet

With one hand take hold of the rail of the chair gently but firmly with your thumb opposite, say, the second finger, with the fingers and thumb straight and pointing downward. Repeat for the other hand.

Your wrists should be directed inward, and your elbows out and slightly down

Direct your shoulders to release away from each other and direct that release to extend to your arms and fingertips

Move your arms up and down to check that you are not making any unnecessary tension

Think of a gentle forearm pull from your fingers to the elbows and then direct the upper parts of your arms to widen away from the chest as your back widens

Think of lifting and stretching the rail of the chair as if it was a piece of elastic, whilst your feet release into the floor

In carrying out hands over the back of a chair you want to use the very minimum amount of muscular effort required. As Alexander pointed out you need to be especially careful not to activate the powerful flexor muscles in your upper body, such as the biceps in your upper arms, or the pectorals in the front of your chest.

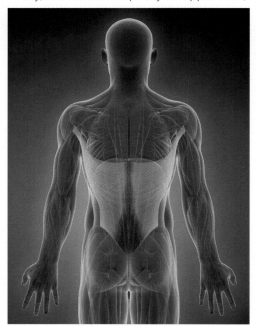

Instead the action of these muscles should be inhibited, with most of the active work falling on *lengthening* extensor muscles on the back of your upper arms (the triceps) and your back, especially the flat, triangular-shaped latissimi dorsi. The result is that your hands release *indirectly* away from each other as the torso widens (though you can also amplify that effect with an appropriate direction for the hands).

You can stay in monkey with your hands over the back of the chair until you start to get tired or start to feel uncomfortable. Obviously in a lesson I will advise you depending on what I can see and feel with my hands. However if you are performing this activity by yourself it is a good idea to use a mirror to

Above The latissimus dorsi muscles

The latissimus dorsi muscles

Alexander rarely mentioned the function or role of specific muscles in his writings but he made an exception in his account of hands over the back of a chair. So it's worth noting that each latissimus dorsi muscle runs from your lower back, travelling up around the outside of the rib cage to pass through your armpit (axilla) and attaches to the inner side your upper-arm bone (humerus), just below the shoulder joint. The latissimi dorsi lie just under your skin so you can easily locate them by using your fingers and thumb to pinch the widest part of your back behind your arm pits. Although relatively thin, they are the widest and most powerful of your back muscles, and the only ones that connect your pelvis to your upper limbs.

You use the latissimus dorsi muscles is in a variety of trunk, shoulder and arm movements, including side and back bending, or when you draw an arm downward and backward, move it towards the side of your body, or rotate it inwards. Some anatomists classify the latissimi dorsi as climbing muscles, but they are also employed in other dynamic, high-intensity movements such as walking, running, rowing, throwing, dancing, and the front crawl and butterfly (which is why they are sometimes called 'the swimming muscles'). Additionally, although not primary breathing muscles, the latissimi dorsi assist with contraction and expansion of the rib cage.

You will appreciate that because of their size the latissimus dorsi muscles can both lengthen and widen your torso, or alternatively they can shorten and narrow it. So learning how to achieve a releasing stretch in the latissimi dorsi (and other deeper back muscles) through the hands over the back of a chair procedure means that not only can you apply that insight to the performance of the specialist hand-arm activities already highlighted, but also to a wide variety of everyday movements, including opening a fridge door, removing clothes from a washing machine, pulling weeds out of the ground, using a hand on a bannister to pull you up the stairs, or driving a car. It bears repeating that acquiring the kinaesthetic skill that allows you to use the least amount of effort in any arm activity is very important not only in itself, but also because chronically stiff, short, misused latissimi dorsi, are often implicated in neck, shoulder, middle or lower back pain, loss of muscle strength, reduced range of movement, and can contribute to problems such as scoliosis and rounded shoulders.

monitor what is going on. The moment you observe yourself drooping, collapsing or stiffening, it is time to come back to upright. As I have mentioned before in the Alexander Technique there is nothing to be gained – neither virtue nor merit – in unnecessary suffering.

When you take your hands off the rail of the chair do so one at a time by un-gripping your fingers, with an open wrist, your arm moving slowly sideways, the elbow leading, with your fingertips releasing in the opposite direction. Your arm is then supported by your open shoulder girdle and elastically strengthened back. There should be no disturbance of the balance of your head on the top of your spine. Follow the same sequence for your other arm so that both arms end up hanging by your sides. Then come back to upright.

Hands over the back of a chair in sitting

The basic procedure for hands over the back of a chair in sitting is more or less the same as in standing except that you are using two chairs, one to sit on and one to put your hands on. You want to arrive in sitting in a lengthened rather than a collapsed state, so ensure that you inhibit and give your orders before sitting down. It's probably best to sit so that your body is supported by the back of the chair (though if you have short legs try sitting in the middle or towards the front of the seat) with your toes turned out slightly and your knees directed forwards and away, complemented by the heels going back and down. You are now facing the back of the second chair.

While you remain sitting upright place your hands one at a time on the top rail of the chair in front of you making sure that you do not lock your elbows. As in hands over the back of a chair in standing you want to ensure that your downward-pointing fingers and thumbs are kept straight and your wrists, which ideally are flat and organised as a continuation of your arms, maintain a slight inward curve opposing the elbows which are curving outwards. Rather than rely on feeling while you are sitting you are in an ideal position to use your eyes to check that this is actually happening.

When you are perched on your sitting bones in a state of balance allow yourself to rotate forward as a unit from your hip joints all the time being careful not to contract the (adductor) muscles on the inside and the back of the thighs that will pull together your knees, or lose your heel contact. If you can successfully maintain all the directions, allow yourself to return slowly back to upright by releasing up and back away from your heels and then rotate forwards again ensuring that your wrists maintain an inward curve and the elbows do not go above the horizontal. Those movements should result in a lengthening and a widening of your back musculature, which in turn will allow your arms and legs to release out of your trunk, indirectly allowing freer and deeper breathing.

Variations on hands over the back of a chair

There are a number of variations possible with your hands placed over the back of a chair. Here are two.

Going up on to the toes

First, if you are performing hands over the chair in monkey you might wish to try going on to your toes. In carrying this out it is very important not to lean on your hands and fingers. In fact you will find that if you are successfully maintaining the thought of 'lift and stretch' of the rail of the chair, that 'up' direction will prevent you pushing downward on to your hands. You should also find that balancing while on your toes is relatively easy to maintain if your thumbs oppose the middle fingers, and you are directing your knees forward and away and your ankles toward one another.

Spiralling

The second variation involves you placing the hands over the back of the chair in either sitting or standing. I will then move the chair either to your left or right, while you follow, elastically adjusting to the movement, without moving your feet. At some point I will ask you to remove both your hands from the rail of the chair. If you have maintained freedom in your torso and legs you will swing back in the direction from where you have travelled, and beyond. That can set up a nice pattern of oscillation for a few seconds, or even longer. Enjoy the experience of the double–spiral musculature working!

Using the arms and hands in everyday life

Non-doing arms and hands

In everyday life we are not always actively using the arms. If you are sitting alone in an armchair or on a sofa listening to the radio or watching the television your hands can rest in a wide variety of positions – in your lap or on the furniture – and release into the contact surfaces rather than being held away from them. You can also monitor your primary control and include the idea of releasing in your armpits and directing your shoulders to release away from each other in order to prevent unnecessary tension.

Active arms and hands

Hand and arm activities can become challenging though when they demand muscular strength. Performing such movements with malcoordination over time can contribute to what biologists call fluctuating asymmetry, a measure of the degree of deviation of how much your body deviates from perfect symmetry in several body parts, such as your arms, legs, feet, fingers, eyes and ears.

Rather than having a checklist for many different activities it is worth thinking in general terms about what needs to happen and what needs to be avoided when using your hands in grasping and manipulating objects. For example, when you take your mobile phone out of your pocket, use a sharp knife for cutting fruit and vegetables, shake hands with someone, or play the piano the danger is that if your arms are not directed towards extension and properly connected

Above A woman preparing food

into the back before making contact, the act of reaching will pull you towards the object and you will pull your head down on to your neck, lose contact with the ground and lose height.

As we learnt earlier the good news is that the principles underlying performing hands on the back of a chair are directly applicable to any activity that involves your arms and hands. Although to an outside observer hands over the back of a chair might look static the directions are dynamic and very similar whether the arms are still or moving. It does not matter whether you are sitting and reading a book, standing and using a bow and arrow or climbing a rock face, it is the relationship between your efficiently working primary control and limbs that counts.

The way to use your arms and hands in any type of manipulation is to inhibit, give the directions for the primary control and allow the release in your neck, head and back to extend through your arms and legs towards the hands and feet. Then direct and allow your hands to open before reaching and then grasping an object. In this way, you will be able to activate your flexor musculature with the minimum amount of effort required.

> ### Using your arms and hands in handling objects
>
> *Look out*
>
> *Inhibit and give your orders for the primary control*
>
> *Order your shoulders to release and widen away from each other, and allow that release to travel to your arms and hands*
>
> *Use a grip in which your fingers are lengthening, using the minimum amount of flexion and effort required*
>
> *Maintain contact with the ground or other support surface at all times*

Below Using a smartphone with hunched shoulders

Opening a door

Let's look at a couple of practical examples to help make this clearer. After you have had number of lessons in the Alexander Technique I will ask you to show me how you normally open a door. Interestingly nearly everyone I see stands too far from the handle, where it is certainly possible to open a door with good coordination, partly because of the capacity of the shoulder girdle to rotate, which allows extension of the arm and hand while maintaining heel contact with the ground. Nevertheless standing away from the door increases the likelihood that you will go off-balance. Typically when reaching toward the door handle you will end up on the balls of the feet because your body is being pulled forward and your head pulled back in a desperate attempt by your brain to achieve a counterbalance to stop you falling.

Clearly it is not in your interest to contract every time you open a door. So, inhibit your reaction to the stimulus to open it and give the directions for the primary control and make a fresh decision whether you wish to continue. Assuming you do, direct your shoulders to release away from each other, and open your hand without stiffening or bending the wrist, and allow the fingertips to lead your arm into length.

Now think of your hand releasing into the handle, your wrist curving slightly inwards and your elbow slightly outwards, at the same time as your head and spine are releasing upward, the whole of your upper arm and back musculature is widening and your feet, especially your heels, release into the ground. Gently press down, or in the case of a doorknob allow rotation in the wrist, without stiffening your thumb or other fingers and without raising or pulling down your shoulder. If you are successful in maintaining your directions your whole body will be engaged in the movement and the door – even a heavy door – will open easily.

Brushing your teeth

Brushing the teeth is something most of us do once or twice daily. Very few of us, though, give much thought to what's involved. Instead we simply grab the toothbrush, apply toothpaste and start scrubbing.

Here's a better way to do it. Pause and give your directions for your neck, head and back, order your shoulders to release into width and let that muscular release extend into your arms and hands so that your fingers and thumbs are also able to release. Allow the fingertips of your chosen hand to lead and pick up the toothbrush using a beak-like grip, your thumb opposite the first or second finger, similar to that in performing hands over the back of a chair.

Above A man brushing his teeth with a power grip and pulling his head back

Initially it might seem a bit odd because you are using an extensor grip, but stay with it. You can then let your fingertips lead your other hand to the tube of toothpaste, and squeeze some on the brush. Always direct the head of the toothbrush to lead your hand to your mouth, which is now opening as your jaw releases forward and down from the jaw joints. In order to clean different areas the brush can be manoeuvred into different positions and your thumb, in conjunction with your very flexible wrist, can oppose different fingers as appropriate. You can also switch hands, of course. One big advantage of cleaning your teeth in this way is that you will use just the right amount of pressure, without any risk of wearing away the gums, or even worse, the teeth themselves.

Thinking about thinking in activity

You might think using the arms and hands in the ways discussed means there is an awful lot to think about in carrying out simple everyday activities. Initially it does take more attention and time than normal, but that's the case with any consciously acquired skill, whether it is learning to drive a car, or finely chop an onion with a very sharp knife.

But the good news – the payoff, in other words – is that remembering to use open hands, with directed, lengthening fingers and thumbs in conjunction with an improved working of the primary control to reach and pick up or manipulate objects can very quickly become part of your repertoire of thinking in activity. All you are doing, after all, is remembering to release your hands without stiffening your wrists – slowly at first but more quickly when you have learned what's involved – while directing or monitoring your head, neck and back, and your contact with the ground or other support surface.

You might consider thinking through the sequence involved in any activity employing your arms and hands which you do a lot – driving a car, riding a bike, or using a computer or mobile device, for instance – while *not* performing it. So when you have some spare time, while travelling on a bus or train, work out in the abstract and then memorise what's involved in a particular movement applying the universal skill of using your limbs in conjunction with an integrated head, neck and back. Then try it out in real-time. Modify things as appropriate.

The challenge of expressive behaviour

The hands over the back of a chair procedure is not only concerned with the manipulation and control of objects. Arms and hands, and other parts of the body, are used by people of all cultures to express thoughts, emotions and intentions, with or without accompanying speech. So whether you are a world-renowned classical pianist, a hip-hop performer, or just

Above Thumbs up

going about your everyday social business, one way or another you will use your arms and hands, as well as the rest of your body, to communicate to others sometimes simple sometimes complex meanings, on a continuum lying somewhere between motion and stillness. But whatever the activity in which you are involved it is surely to your advantage to be able to express yourself, even very dramatically, by maintaining openness and elasticity in your shoulder girdle, arms and hands.

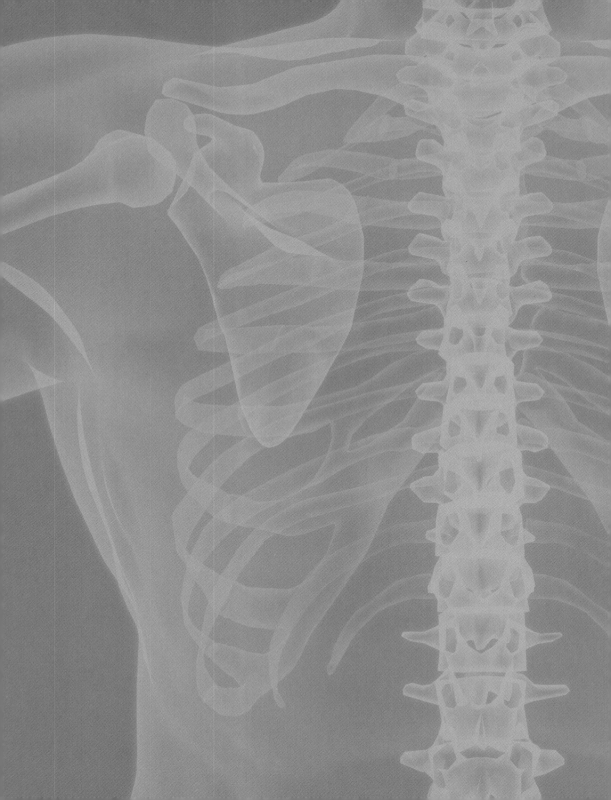

Chapter 9 – *Lying down*

'Let the individual recline in static security for 15 to 20 minutes after luncheon in the supine position on a carpeted floor with the head resting as comfortably as possible on one or more books forming a hard bolster … and the feet brought as close to the buttocks as is possible without muscular strain (knees in the air and slightly abducted, elbows on the floor and the hands resting on the junction of thorax and abdomen). This brief midday rest induces a gradual relaxation or inhibition of the sacrospinalis mass and all the extensor musculature of the body and a temporary release from their inevitable state of torsional strain'

Raymond Dart

Lying on the flat of our backs without the need to use the arms for balance or support is something to which most of us do not give much thought. Perhaps we should. Recent research shows that our ability to adopt that position as infants distinguishes us from other animals, including apes. Whereas an infant chimpanzee has the strength and physical maturity to cling to its mother 24 hours a day for the first few months of life the human newborn does not. The result is that we are carried around, often a considerable burden for our mothers, who may need to look after additional small children, whilst juggling other responsibilities.

Of course child-rearing practices and their impact on the development of motor skills vary considerably cross-culturally, but in our society infants often find themselves placed on their backs. But what is lost in terms of body contact is hopefully made up through intense face-to-face interaction, such as eye contact, smiling, vocalisation, imitation, touching and hand gestures between the child and its mother and other people.

In fact as you matured but before you learnt to roll over and crawl your hands began to explore your head, face, and the hugely important relationship between the limbs. You also explored other objects such as the clothes you were wearing and the toys you were given. That on-going cycle of activity in infancy very quickly led to you developing a high level of self-awareness, including a keenly attuned proprioceptive sense. In short, the legacy produced by lying in a stable supine position in infancy was a key factor in the development of your physical and social intelligence.

At any age lying down on the back or on the side creates the conditions for rest and sleep, processes which conserve energy and facilitate the management and repair of the body's complex neurophysiological systems. We know from fossil records that our early ancestors in

southern Africa slept in groups on the ground, using mats made from grasses and aromatic leaves. A similar pattern is found amongst contemporary hunter-gatherers. At night in the dry season warm-climate foragers such as the Hadza will lie on an impala skin covered by a thin shawl and sleep in full view of one another at the centre of the camp, partly as a protection against dangerous predators, such as lions, leopards and other wild animals, and partly as an activity that promotes social bonding.

Above A baby lying on her back playing with her feet

By contrast, in our society lying down is rarely performed in a public setting. We only tend to carry it out when we are very ill, drunk, sunbathing or delayed at airports. Typically lying down takes place indoors in the privacy of the home. When most of us think of it the chances are that ideas of sleep will come to mind. By contrast, in the Alexander Technique the practice of lying down has never been concerned with slumber, though most people find the activity very relaxing – and some may drop off!

Although its physical aspect has been copied by any number of disciplines, including branches of yoga and Pilates, Alexander lying down is only truly meaningful as part of the technique. The reason is that from its inception the practice was never solely about assuming a resting position, or closing the eyes to experience 'quiet wakefulness'. Instead, it was dubbed 'inhibition work'. It involved Alexander or one of his assistants putting a student on a table, or the floor and explaining, 'Now, I'm going to move your arm (or your leg). You're to say "no", while you give your directions for the primary control and allow me to move it without your interfering with it.' Alexander also stressed that throughout the period of lying down a student's eyes were to be kept open, engaging with the world, in part because of the important role the visual sense plays in maintaining balance.

The fear of falling

Above Raymond Dart (1893-1988)

'In precariously-poised man that ever-present fear of the livelong day (and of sleeping hours also in many individuals) is that of falling,' wrote Raymond Dart, who considered it to be our primary fear, upon which other anxieties and phobias are constructed. Whether true or not there can be no doubt that any sense of losing one's balance stimulates powerful neurophysiological mechanisms, including the release of stress hormones and a stiffening of the body's musculature. Whilst a toddler can take a tumble and escape with nothing more than a bruise, we run the risk of a serious and very occasionally fatal injury. The central nervous system will do everything within its power to maintain uprightness if, for example, you slip on a banana skin, or trip on a loose paving stone in order to prevent your head hitting the ground.

After starting a course of lessons in the Alexander Technique in 1943, Dart, then 50 and suffering from such a degree of fatigue and exhaustion that he had been forced to take a year's sabbatical from his post as Director of the School of Anatomy at the University of the Witwatersrand, was quick to appreciate the relevance of lying down for his and other people's health and well-being. One of first things that became apparent to him was the usefulness of Alexander lying down in eliminating or, at least, reducing the fear of falling.

The importance of the neck muscles in maintaining balance

The idea that interference with structures in the neck can lead to instability in walking and upright movements was first proposed by scientists in the late 19th century and confirmed by experiments by neurophysiologists in the early 1960s. In order to update the science, in the early 1990s a small number of senior researchers in different laboratories throughout the world bravely volunteered to have a local anaesthetic injected into the muscles of one side of the neck so as to understand better the role of the large number of receptors or spindles in the relevant muscles and joints.

One interesting effect was that it gave subjects an illusion of falling or being drawn toward the side which had been injected. In fact, all those involved in the experiment found it very difficult to maintain balance while standing and walking. One researcher reported that he felt he was acting 'very much like a drunken person'. Later when he lay on a couch, he had a strong sensation that it was toppling over toward the side of his neck which had been anaesthetised.

The important lesson from this study, and also from recent more general research on the impact of anaesthesia on the human body, is that the nerve receptors in the muscles and joints of the neck relay highly important sensory inputs to the brain in maintaining uprightness and balance, directly comparable to the semi-circular or vestibular canals of the inner ear. 'Thus the scientific evidence accords with Alexander's observation that the state of the neck muscles, and therefore the relation of the head to the trunk, is of primary importance,' concluded lead researcher Dr Garlick.

It's also worth noting that your neck contains a variety of mechanisms which contribute to the control of normal breathing and blood flow into your limbs.

Continued practice led Dart to reflect on some of the other advantages of what he called the 'semi-supine, flexed position' for those such as him suffering from the effects of an exaggerated spinal curvature, manifested in rounded shoulders, scoliosis and lordosis. In his 1946 paper *The Postural Aspect of Malocclusion* Dart explained that semi-supine has a number of advantages. Firstly, it encourages neurological inhibition of the bad habits which promote bodily asymmetry. Secondly, it re-trains the support and contact areas of the body, such as the occipital area at the back of the head, shoulder blades, hip bones and feet, to share the business of supporting body weight, which in turn helps in the physical de-rotation of our twisted bodies. Thirdly, lying on a firm surface generates a significant degree of sensory input into the extensor musculature of the back that is difficult to achieve on a soft surface such as a conventional mattress.

Like Alexander, Dart did not believe that the myriad problems associated with compression and asymmetry of the body, including weak and inflexible backs, in otherwise healthy people are caused by genetic or structural defects. Instead he calculated that they are largely functional in origin, caused either by misuse or disuse.

The encouraging news is that the stable semi-supine position allows us to recapture at least some of that finely tuned proprioceptive sense that most of us developed as infants lying on our backs, further refined as we grew into energetic and inquisitive toddlers, but which, for a variety of reasons, we then lost as we got older. In particular Alexander lying down helps to promote a conscious level of integration in muscle groups that are required in complex movements performed when we are upright.

Alexander lying down in a lesson

It starts with inhibition

Because of the expertise he had developed with his hands, Alexander rarely used lying down in his lessons preferring to guide students in and out of the chair and a variety of other procedures, such as monkey or going on to the toes. However when he did perform table work great emphasis was placed on ensuring that the student's neck was free, the head was properly supported by a pile of books and the shoulders were releasing away from each other. Then Alexander would work on freeing and getting length in the powerful leg muscles, all the while checking that the student was not holding the breath by locking the rib cage.

Alexander was meticulous in teaching the practice of lying down to his early assistants and the students on his teacher training course. The explicit instruction he gave to both groups was to work with a student in the chair, followed by table work and then to return to the chair. If there were still significant problems, the advice was to put the student back on the table to see if any further release could be obtained.

Nowadays Alexander teachers vary in how much emphasis is placed on lying down on the teaching table. Some carry it out at the beginning of a lesson and then switch to the chair, while others start with the chair and finish with the table. Of course a lot also depends on the needs of the individual student. Someone suffering from chronic lower back pain, a 'frozen' shoulder, tennis elbow or poor balance is in quite a different situation to a runner who is pain free and wants to explore aspects of the body's spiral mechanism in order to improve her running style. In this case, it is possible there might be no lying down in a lesson.

Whenever lying down does take place, however, inhibition and direction should always guide the process from the outset. For example, in a lesson when you are sitting on the

Alexander table (or floor) with either your knees bent or out in front of you and about to lie down it is very important to think about how you are about to unroll, even though hands-on assistance is being provided. If you do not consider how you perform the movement in this situation the likelihood is that you will not think about it when you perform lying down on your own. Most probably you will unroll in a habitual way and finish by pushing your head into the books, the opposite of what is meant to happen.

So look out, inhibit and direct and then support yourself with the flat of your hands pointing out to the side or behind you, being careful not to hunch your shoulders. Order your neck

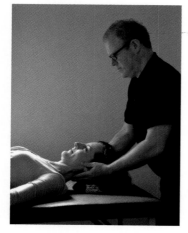

muscles at the base of the skull to release so that your head goes forward and up and the back lengthens and widens, and then think of your tummy falling back into your lower back. Pause for a moment. Now without stiffening or tightening your legs, let your lengthening spine uncurl from the tailbone, vertebra by vertebra, all the while ensuring that you are not holding your breath. With my hands I will provide the right amount of support for your body weight.

Towards the end of the movement it is important that you do not collapse or become a dead weight. You also want to ensure that your head does not reach the books before your neck so that the lengthening along the spine is not compromised in any way.

Above Alexander-lying down in a lesson

The optimum height of books

The height of books needed to support your head at the beginning of a lesson will depend on your overall body shape. A good general rule is that the height of the pile of books required should be just enough that your head does not fall back, but not so much that your chin is being forced down. Some people, such as ballet dancers with over-straightened necks, require only a small amount of support, while others suffering from over-curvature of the cervical and thoracic vertebrae, which can be caused by conditions such as osteoporosis, ankylosing spondylitis, Scheurmann's disease or postural kyphosis, will need a great deal more.

In a lesson the best arrangement is for the lower part of the back of your head (the occiput) to be near the front edge of the pile of books. That not only ensures that your neck muscles are free to release and let go of the head thereby developing better tone, but also allows me to place my hands on a greater surface area of your neck.

As the lesson continues and more release in the musculature takes place it is possible that some of the books will need to be removed so that your chin does not press into your throat.

Guided movements

I will perform a series of hands-on adjustments to your neck, head, shoulders and limbs that were developed by Alexander and other teachers. These guided movements are very different to the sort of manipulations performed by chiropractors, osteopaths and physiotherapists. There are at least three reasons for this. Firstly, unlike therapists, an Alexander teacher has been taught to employ inhibition and direction in his own body-self before making any contact with a student.

Secondly, while therapists largely focus on curing a specific ailment, say, in your neck, shoulder, elbow, lower back, or knee, my aim is to teach you an improved general coordination and kinaesthetic sense which can then be used in your everyday life, not just in a lesson. That said, a therapy may be necessary. I know from experience that people, say, suffering from spinal stenosis, badly sprained ankles and dislocated kneecaps, require the right sort of treatment from experienced medical professionals. However, once any severe pain or swelling has reduced and there is reasonable mobility it is a great advantage for a student to learn how to maintain better balance and symmetry in movement, so that any protective compensation that may have developed, say, whilst using a walking stick or wearing a leg cast does not result in a permanent change in gait.

Thirdly, the guided hands-on movements I perform are always very gentle. There is no pulling, prodding, rocking, or high and low velocity thrusts involved. Nor is there any significant deep pressure manipulation of the soft tissue, including muscles, ligaments and fascia, found in various types of bodywork such as Hellerwork, Postural Integration or Rolfing.

In an Alexander lesson you are encouraged to think of the mental directions for the primary control and to link these up with orders for other body parts before and while allowing slow, simple movements, such as flexing the hip joint, extending a leg, or taking the arm out to the side or above the head, while not losing a sense of time and space. Sometimes I will also ask you to give the orders for the primary control and then also think of a release between body parts indicated by my hands – this could be between the top of one knee and the back of your same side rib cage, or the topmost boney part on one side of your pelvis (iliac crest) and the lower border of your rib cage, either on the same or opposite side without any overt movement occurring. Throughout the process you are an active participant linking up mental directions with improved sensory experiences delivered by my hands. Over time that will undoubtedly have an impact on the arrangement of your body's deep tissue, but it will happen indirectly because through inhibition and direction there will be an improvement in your coordination and proprioception.

Lying down by yourself

The importance of Alexander lying down

Some students of the technique, even those with chronic neck, shoulder and back pain, are highly resistant to the idea of carrying out the recommended one or more daily sessions of Alexander lying down. Why? Some tell me that they consider the practice is too passive to get to the root of their problems; they feel that they need to strengthen muscles by being up and about performing exercise (or exercises) of one kind or another. Some think that sleep provides all the lying down that is required. Others reveal that they feel guilty about 'doing nothing' – 'Women are taught to be industrious,' one of my female students, a 60-year-old secondary school teacher, told me recently (blame the Protestant work ethic, I suppose).

But these perceptions are based on a profound misunderstanding of how the body-mind continuum works. We have already learnt how important the stable supine position is in infancy. The stable semi-supine position also has far-reaching effects for older children and adults because it provides an opportunity, since the spine is not weight-bearing, to allow the body's musculature to release towards a full and natural length.

Longer lives, shortened spines

Given that we are now living around twice as long as early modern humans (most adults died between the age of 30 and 40), Alexander lying down undoubtedly bestows profound 'physical' benefits in terms of the health and repair of the musculoskeletal system, especially the 23 sponge-like intervertebral discs. Made up of 88 per cent water they constitute around one third of the length of the spine and play a critical role as shock absorbers in everyday movement, especially in bending and twisting motions. The discs are also vital in absorbing compressive pressures in specialist movements such as lifts performed by weight lifters and jumps carried out by dancers and athletes. Without the protection of the discs our spines would suffer irreparable damage.

← **Normal Disc**

← **Degenerative Disc**

← **Bulging Disc**

← **Herniated Disc**

← **Thinning Disc**

← **Disc Degeneration with Osteophyte Formation**

Above Different spinal conditions

The average person's height can vary significantly throughout the day depending on how much fluid is in the discs. Typically maximum height is achieved in the morning after someone climbs out of bed and the minimum in the evening after the daily round after gravity has compressed the spine. The difference can be as much as three quarters of an inch (1.9 cm).

Over time those compressed discs stiffen as the blood supply and microcirculation diminishes. Obesity, diabetes and smoking amplify the problem. According to world-renowned neurosurgeon Dr Roger Härtl it's not uncommon for people to lose two inches (5 cm) in height by the age of 60 because of disc degeneration. In turn that can lead to a collapse of the spinal vertebrae, causing significant pain, and damage to the nerves and spinal cord. It can also result in a hunched shape, kyphosis and a protruding stomach that interferes with digestion and free breathing. The lesson is that it is clearly in your long-term interests to look after your spine by performing regular sessions of Alexander lying down. In that way any body fluid that has been squeezed out of the spinal discs by compression has a chance to be reabsorbed.

Grounding

There are other benefits in carrying out the stable semi-supine procedure. Not only does it have a beneficial and restorative effect on the functioning of the internal organs, but the long-standing experience of Alexander teachers and students indicates that it has a soothing or 'grounding' effect. Why should this be? As we already know humans are the only primates that are capable of standing and walking fully upright. By becoming bipedal our early ancestors with brains little larger than that of a modern ape exposed the most vulnerable part of themselves – the front of the body, including the eyes, throat, belly and

genitals – to the possibility of attack from extremely competitive fellow hominins and a multitude of carnivorous creatures, such as sabre-toothed cats and enormous hyenas.

Our brains have grown enormously over the intervening several million years, but that biological legacy of our fronts facing forward when we are upright remains. Although relatively few of us routinely confront dangerous wild animals in our everyday interactions with people and the material environment, if we feel threatened physically, emotionally, intellectually or even financially,

Above A representation of an early hominin

we tend to tighten our musculature (and joints), either on a temporary or permanent basis. A significant effect of that stiffening of the muscles is interference with the flow of electrical messages to the brain, which degrades the proprioceptive sense. All these factors combine to have a profound effect on the efficiency, smoothness and speed of our movements. But one of the great benefits of Alexander lying down is that it recalibrates your body-mind's 'danger system', reducing the 'fight or flight' or 'startle pattern' response. Put another way it helps you to get back in touch with your body, open up to the world and restore balanced movement.

That chimes with a fascinating recent discovery by neuropsychologist Eddie Harmon-Jones about the way the attitude of our bodies affects emotions and behaviour. In a novel experiment involving 46 first-year university students (23 male and 23 female) using an electroencephalograph (EEG) to measure electrical activity in the brain, he found that while all subjects became irritated or angry after being subjected to an insult about their intelligence and likeability, those who were sitting upright were much more liable to act on their feelings and retaliate compared with those who were lying flat on their backs. The result which surprised many cognitive scientists suggests that body position interacts with and influences how the brain processes a range of emotions – in our culture not only feelings of anger and aggression but also, more speculatively, desire and happiness.

Little wonder that on the basis of this and his other studies Dr Harmon-Jones quotes approvingly the directive given by the Prophet Muhammad to his followers: 'When one of you becomes angry while standing, he should sit down. If the anger leaves him, well and good; otherwise he should lie down.' That was good advice 1400 years ago and it is good advice now. Indeed, it underpins why Alexander lying down, involving inhibition and direction, lends itself very well to cultivating a more 'laid-back' approach to life – even when you are upright!

Performing Alexander lying down

Alexander lying down is best performed on a daily basis on a reasonably firm but resilient surface such as a carpeted floor – in general a bed is too soft and some might find that a wooden or stone floor is too hard. It can also be carried out more than once a day if you have time, or if there is a need. The optimum time to spend in Alexander lying down is about 20 minutes. However, some time spent in Alexander lying down is better than no time at all, so even a few minutes will create substantial benefits.

Bear in mind that throughout the time spent in Alexander lying down you are not trying to achieve a state of 'heavy' relaxation. Instead you are trying to allow yourself to release into the contact surfaces so that your whole body is supported. Choose a quiet spot where it is warm and free from drafts.

Above Lying down the Alexander way

If you find that you consistently fall asleep during Alexander lying down, especially when performing it in the afternoon and early evening, it usually indicates that you are carrying a significant sleep debt. Do not ignore it; sleep is very important for your health and well-being. Try to go to bed a little earlier until the urge to sleep while performing semi-supine disappears.

Getting on to the floor

There are many good ways of getting on the floor. Probably the easiest way is to perform a deep squat, although I can show you other ways if that is not possible. The challenge for most of us is that as soon we start to even think of lying down we begin to crouch or stoop. The only way to solve this problem is to inhibit and direct – and mean it! Thinking of coming up and back from the ankles before bending the knees often helps as it is releasing in the opposite direction that you intend to move. So too does taking your time and not rushing.

Place your feet a good distance apart with the toes turned well out. Keep inhibiting, give plenty of orders, and allow your knees to release gently and steadily over the feet in such a way that you come down vertically while maintaining lengthening and widening in your torso – that is, move as far as you can without effort or strain. Do it in stages if you find that it makes it easier. Now allow your torso to rotate forward slowly from the hip joints and let your knees continue to release forward and away, all the while monitoring the primary control and maintaining contact with your heels for as long as possible. Your shoulder blades should lie flat on the back throughout the movement, your arms hanging forward.

As you get near the floor you can make contact with either your knuckles (like an ape) or the palms of your hands (like a monkey) so that you end up on all fours. Now put both knees to the left or right and lie on your side before rolling over so that your head is supported by the books. If you have missed the target direct and open the fingers of one hand and let it travel up the midline of your torso to support and lift the weight of your head so that you can move the books into position with your other hand. Slowly lower your head, being careful to allow your neck to drop down first. Then place your arms by your sides with the palms of your hands facing the floor, the wrists turned in towards your body and the elbows out to the side.

The legs

At the moment your legs, which make up around a third of your body weight, are extended. If they are not already doing so allow them to find a neutral position each using their own weight to spiral outward and away from your hip joints. You are now going to move your legs. First, however, look out so that you are aware of the ceiling (or sky if outdoors) as this is the direction to which your knees are going to point. Do keep in mind that you can stop at any point in the process and start again especially if you register any disturbance around your neck and head, or if you find that you are pulling the back in or fixing your breathing. Additionally you want to ensure that your feet do not slip away from you when you are lying down. That will happen if your socks or stockings do not create sufficient grip on the surface you are lying on. Using bare feet (or shoes) prevents this.

Now gently and slowly point forward the toes of one foot without overextending them, while consciously aiming up through the back or underside of your knee towards the ceiling in such a way that the heel slides backwards ending up comfortably near your sitting bones. Then let that foot make full contact with the floor, especially through the heel, being careful not to stiffen your ankle joint. Inhibit and direct and then perform the same movement with your other leg. In order to minimise the risk of creating too much tension in your legs your feet should be positioned more or less shoulder-width apart, with the toes turned out slightly.

At this juncture you might find that you have got a small arch in your lower back. Do not be tempted to flatten it. If you wait a few moments it will often adjust and settle down. If that does not happen, or you are experiencing on-going tightness in your hip joints and lower back, gently and slowly flex your toes upwards and bring one leg at a time, upwards, in a slow, open movement towards your chest. Once both legs are in place allow your fingertips to lead the hands in such a way that they wrap either around your knee, or at the back of your lower thigh. Be careful though not to have too tight a grip as that will result in a narrowing or contraction of your shoulders. You can then slowly and gently draw your legs a little way (not all the way unless you are very flexible) towards your chest and hold them for a few seconds or longer. When you come to put each leg down, you will need to flex your toes upwards again, and then direct the front of your heel to lead a slow and smooth movement towards the support of the floor.

Over time Alexander lying down will help your chronically shortened leg muscles release into length, so that your legs are able to rotate freely either outwards or inwards, while getting a better connection with the musculature of your torso.

The arms

The arms can be placed by your sides supported by the floor. However if you find this is not very comfortable, especially if the shoulder and wrist of your dominant arm rise up, place your open hands, palms down, on the pelvis or the tummy, the elbows out to the sides. You can also position the hands, palms down, on the upper chest with your fingertips just below the collarbones near the breastbone. This will bring your elbows nearer the torso and has the advantage of opening and stimulating the lower ribs, which is beneficial to your breathing. Another option if you are round-shouldered, or just want some extra support, is to place your arms, hands palm up, out to the sides at shoulder level making a right angle.

> ### Getting down on to the floor
>
> *Look out*
>
> *Assume a wide base with your toes turned out*
>
> *Inhibit any desire to stoop or crouch in the direction of the pile of books*
>
> *Give your directions for the primary control*
>
> *Order an upward release through your ankles, knees and hips*
>
> *Come up and back a little from your ankle joints*
>
> *Allow your knees to release forward and away over your feet while maintaining the directions for your head, neck and back*
>
> *Allow your hands to open and make contact with the floor so that you are on all fours*
>
> *Roll over so that your head is supported by the books*
>
> *Allow your knees to bend so that they are pointing to the ceiling, your feet positioned around shoulder-width apart, with your toes turned out slightly*
>
> *Place your arms by your torso, or on the pelvis or tummy*

Awareness of your body's support points

If you have had a particularly busy or stressful day you might wish to lie on the floor for a few minutes and gradually bring your attention back to yourself. One very good way to encourage that to happen, as Dart suggested, is to become aware of your body's support points – the bony contact point of your head, the plates of your shoulder blades, the large mass of bone at the base of your spine or pelvis, the knuckle-like bones of your elbows, and the three bony points of contact of your feet, the areas around the heel, big toe and small toe. Start with awareness of your head lightly resting on the books and then your shoulders, the back of your pelvis, your arms and feet in such a way that in the end you have a good sense of support being provided to your whole body, especially your back.

If you are still a little tense even after lying down for some minutes give yourself a stimulus to turn your head either left or right. But first inhibit, soften your gaze and allow your eyes to look at a point on the ceiling while maintaining peripheral vision. Then give permission for your neck to un-grip and very slowly turn your head from side to side, all the time ensuring that its weight is being given to the books and your eyes maintain their direction.

Inhibiting and directing

When you are lying down the basic Alexander directions are: neck free, head forward and up (or out), the whole spine to lengthen from the tailbone right up into the head (more or less behind the eyes), back to widen, and knees to go up to the ceiling (a shorthand for the lengthening of all the muscles from a freely released hip joint to the knee, and all of the

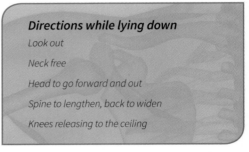

Directions while lying down

Look out

Neck free

Head to go forward and out

Spine to lengthen, back to widen

Knees releasing to the ceiling

muscles from a freely released ankle to the knee). These are to be given altogether, one after the other. You will also find that a big advantage of Alexander lying down is that you are much less likely to 'do' the directions than if you are upright. Also bear in mind that there is no need to give the orders as if you are reading a piece of text. There's no rush. Allow yourself the necessary time to link the thoughts together.

If you find that you are out of shape, you can spend quite a lot of time just asking for your neck muscles to release at the base of the skull before adding on the other orders. A good way to think of your head releasing out is to direct the crown of your head to release behind you. Another useful direction, especially if you have a habit of collapsing or pushing the neck forward, is to order the column of your neck to drop back and down towards the floor, which will connect with the direction for a lengthening release along the spine into your head. You can then add on an order to allow your lumbar area to drop back and down towards the ground.

If you find that your mind is wandering and it is difficult to stay present a useful strategy is to look out, give the orders aloud, and consider what they refer to. That will help bring you into the present.

It's often quite a good idea to remain still for a period of time, just giving your directions, especially for your primary control and legs. Later on you can add on orders for your arms. If they are lying by your sides, the backs of your hands facing upwards, you can direct your shoulders to release away from each other, and then allow that release to flow along your arms toward elbows, wrists and fingertips. You can also think of the directions used in putting hands over the back of a chair. So direct your wrists in, your elbows out and ask for a widening of the upper parts of the arms as your back widens. Without actively doing anything you can then order your fingers and thumbs to lengthen.

Exploring inhibition

Once you are settled you can use the methodology employed by Alexander when he was experimenting and observing himself in front of the mirrors. If your arms are by your side you can entertain the idea that you want to move, say, your left hand so that it is supported by the pelvis. Then you can inhibit and give the directions for the primary control and decide to carry out the movement, do nothing, or perform a different activity – for example, allowing your right or left leg to fall slightly inwards or outwards, or bringing your extended index or other finger to your nose.

Obviously there are a lot of permutations to play with in Alexander lying down, but you do not have to stick to customary Alexander methodology or practices that you have been shown in a lesson. Instead use your imagination. For example, if you are wearing a watch you might want to check the time to find out how long you have been on the floor. When performing this action, inhibit, give the directions for your primary control and then bring the watch to your face rather than as most people do the face to the watch. Try also to pick up any distortion in the relationship between your head, neck and back as you move the arm. You can also explore your use of a mobile phone in the same way. Rather than pull your head down to one side as most people do when taking a call, instead allow your minimally flexed hand, with the fingertips leading, to bring the phone to your ear or in front of your face without disturbing the balance of your head on your neck. Be aware also that there's no need to stiffen your arms and narrow the shoulders as you do so. Similar considerations apply to texting, of course.

All such movements will provide a wealth of information and provide great insight into how you are using your arms and hands while holding and manipulating objects in any number of activities when sitting, standing and walking.

Experimenting with breathing, sounds and speech

Breathing

Because of his successful experience in sorting out his vocal and breathing problems through indirect means Alexander was firmly against the performance of specific breathing exercises. He claimed that it is not only unnecessary but even harmful to 'even think of taking a breath'. Put simply, good breathing is a function of an efficiently working primary control and not an

Above Deep breathing often causes us to stiffen the neck, pull the head back and down and pull the back in

end in itself. I concur for the same reasons as Alexander and this is why I am opposed to so-called deep breathing, the direct manipulation of the breath common in hatha yoga and exercise-based systems such as Pilates ('as you breathe in feel your ribs expanding, and as you breathe out feel your ribs closing'), or any attempt to synchronise breathing with stride rate in running ('inhale for three foot strikes, exhale for two').

The key aspect of improved breathing in the Alexander Technique is based on a very simple principle. You want to create the conditions – good general coordination – under which your rib cage expands and contracts without strain. That eliminates any need to pull or suck air in. You will recall that in Alexander's case breathing in that way caused irritation of the mucous membranes of the throat and nose, as well as inflammation of the vocal cords. It's something we all need to avoid doing, even if we are not professional reciters.

You will also remember that when Alexander was observing himself in front of the mirrors he eventually found that it was the pulling back of the head which was causing the depressing of the larynx and the sucking in of breath rather than the other permutations that he had considered. So while lying on the floor take the opportunity to deliberately rotate your head back and down – do it with a bit of oomph! – so that it pushes into the books. The chances are that not only will you notice the pulling up of your chest and the pulling in of your lower and middle back, but you will also notice that your legs stiffen and your knees are pulled together. You should also observe a significant interference in the breathing pattern because of constriction in your nose and throat triggered by the stiffening of your neck.

It's also worth experimenting with deliberately sniffing in air to find out what happens. So feel free at any point in the breathing cycle to sniff quite sharply air in through your nose. Similarly, you can suck vigorously air in through your mouth. On both occasions you will notice amongst other things an upward movement of your sternum and the rib cage, with your back arching and your head pushed back on to the books. Your rib cage will also stiffen.

These small experiments clearly demonstrate the importance of the head, neck and back relationship in relation to respiration. If your primary control is working inefficiently your breathing will be strained, while if it is working well the result will be an efficiently-moving diaphragm, the dome-shaped muscle that separates your thoracic (chest) cavity from the abdominal cavity, and a coordinated response in the muscles of your rib cage, lungs and abdominal muscles. If everything is set up properly, atmospheric pressure will respond to the partial vacuum created in your lungs at the end of expiration, without you having to do anything directly. 'There is no such thing as breathing as such' was how Alexander summed it up to his students. On the other hand, if you have developed

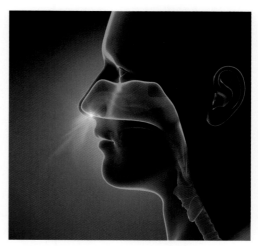

Above Quiet nasal breathing should be the norm

a habit of holding your rib cage in some way you might have to remind yourself to allow your ribs to release so that they can move. As long as there is no physical obstruction, or you are not involved in strenuous activity, smooth and efficient nasal breathing should be the norm.

One of the beneficial effects of practising Alexander lying down is an improvement in the efficiency of the respiratory system through a gradual improvement in general coordination. If

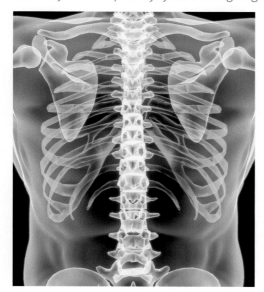

Above Illustration of the rib cage

you are a belly or a top of the chest breather, both of which are inefficient, it will mean a change towards increased elasticity, mobility and flexibility in the way your rib cage works. Once I have detected better movement I will position the back of your fingers lightly against the two pairs of small floating ribs, which lie just beyond half-way down the sides of your torso. That can give you a better sense of what the order 'back (or torso) to widen' entails, in conjunction with an experience of the easy expansion and contraction of your entire rib cage.

In performing this activity by yourself you need to be careful not to raise your shoulders when placing the hands against the floating ribs, or focus or concentrate on the specific area of your torso. Instead maintain the directions for your primary control at the same time as you are using your eyes to look out and take in what's happening in the environment. It's also vital that you do not 'do' anything with your fingers. You are not meant to be actively pushing against or otherwise manipulating your rib cage. It's enough that your breathing is stimulated by the light contact of your fingers against the floating ribs, while you give the appropriate directions to maintain your internal length and width.

Sounds and speech

Chatting with others is something most of us do every day and as we noted earlier Alexander found out in his experiments in front of the mirrors that vocalisation can be done with either good or poor coordination. So take advantage of the information that is available to you while performing Alexander lying down and explore how you communicate. But first, rather than use ordinary speech, make some other sounds. For example, inhibit, give your orders and choose to whistle or hum making sure in the latter case to employ the resonators in your head, throat and chest.

You can then play around with speaking in a normal voice or in a whisper, recite a poem, rehearse a speech you are due to give, sing softly or in full voice, or if you can think of something amusing, experiment with chuckling or laughing. You can also shout as if you were about to warn someone of an impending danger – 'don't lean out the window!' Additionally you can combine speech with the type of gesticulation you use in everyday life and find out what effect that is having on your body as you lie on the floor.

The major problem that most of us have in producing sounds is the interference of the primary balance of the head. Instead

> **Making sounds**
>
> *Look out*
>
> *Inhibit and direct*
>
> *Allow yourself to be supported by the floor*
>
> *Do not take a special breath to begin, but instead use whatever breath you have available*
>
> *Allow your jaw to release forward and down from the jaw joints on either side of your ears and make a sound*
>
> *Stop making a sound well before any excessive tightening of your rib cage takes place*
>
> *Allow your lips to close at the end of expiration so that the air is directed in through your nose*

of leaving the immobile upper jaw where it is in space and allowing the movable lower jaw to release freely forward and down from the jaw joints, located in front of the ears on either side of the head, we do the opposite. That is the lower jaw is more or less fixated and the skull containing the upper jaw is retracted or pulled back. (You will recall that was Alexander's original problem.) It's caused by misuse of the intertwined muscle groups around the movable jaw joints and the balance point of the head on the neck. So it is useful to bear in mind that at rest your jaw needs to hang from the jaw joints, in such a way that there is always a 2 or 3 mm of space between the back molar teeth, the lips in light contact. Also note that your tongue should not be pressed against your teeth, cheek or palate, but should lie quietly on the floor of your mouth.

Above Making sounds often results in pulling the head down on to the neck

Whatever sound you intend to make ensure that you leave your head freely poised on the top of your spine supported by the books and direct either the whole of your jaw or the chin forward and up to the ceiling. The order will prevent your jaw joints tightening and your throat contracting as you open the mouth. It will also indirectly check the pulling back of your head on to the neck.

Keep in mind that you do not want to take a special breath before you start making any sound. Instead just use whatever air is available. Additionally make sure that you do not focus on or suck in breath at the end. A good way to prevent the latter happening is to allow your lips to close lightly at the end of expiration so that the air is directed in through your nose, while thinking of your head remaining poised on top of the spine, and your body supported by the floor.

Another challenge for many of us when conversing with others, especially in formal settings if we are nervous, is that we speak too quickly, which results in interference with the breathing cycle. If that is the case with you experiment, perhaps by reading aloud from a book or reciting a poem and deliberately slow down the rate at which the words come out of your mouth. You can then try this out with family or friends before using it in other situations.

In the process of kinaesthetic learning keep in mind that there is no advantage in actively squeezing the air out of your lungs in speaking (or even in normal breathing). You will only end up losing internal length. Try it out when you are performing Alexander lying down and you will almost certainly experience the shortening and narrowing of your torso and the loss of contact with the floor.

As we have learnt when performing Alexander lying down you ought to be able to detect any depression of your larynx or tightening of the rib cage caused by pulling your head down on to your neck as you exhale or produce sound of one sort or another. If anything like that does happen it will have revealed something very valuable about your habitual production of sounds. Moreover you can be very sure that this pattern of malcoordination is not just happening while you are on the floor but also when you are sitting, standing or walking. Take the opportunity to perform the same range of soundings when sitting or standing in front of the mirror, or ideally mirrors, and observe what happens, especially in the relationship between your head, neck and torso.

Getting up from the floor

There are a variety of good ways of getting back to upright without contracting. Here are three options, all of which should be performed with inhibition and direction. The first is to let your eyes move either left or right and allow your head to follow. Now allow your knees to turn to

Above Getting up from Alexander-lying down

the same side and roll over so that you are on all fours. Walk yourself backwards so that you are now sitting on your haunches. Keep the directions going for the primary control and then allow either your right or left knee to come through so that your foot is on the floor. Allow yourself to think of leaning up and forward slightly from the front ankle and knee which is on the ground, let your legs straighten and come up vertically to standing. If you find that you are pulling down or stiffening as you come to upright, rather than trying to go up vertically, you might find it useful to direct your back up and back and then allow yourself to follow that direction to upright.

A second option is to allow the fingertips of either your left or right hand to lead the arm across your upper torso, while you track the movement with your eyes and then allow your head, followed by the rest of your body to release into the direction of travel. Allow your hand to move on to the floor to the side of your body, and then roll over on to all fours before coming to upright.

A third way is to look up and behind you either to the left or right without moving your head and only then when the eye movement has reached its limit let it turn in the same direction. Allow your eye-led head movement to trigger a spiral movement in the rest of your body so that eventually you end up on all fours. Stand up. Now it's time for you to complete your journey into movement by learning about running!

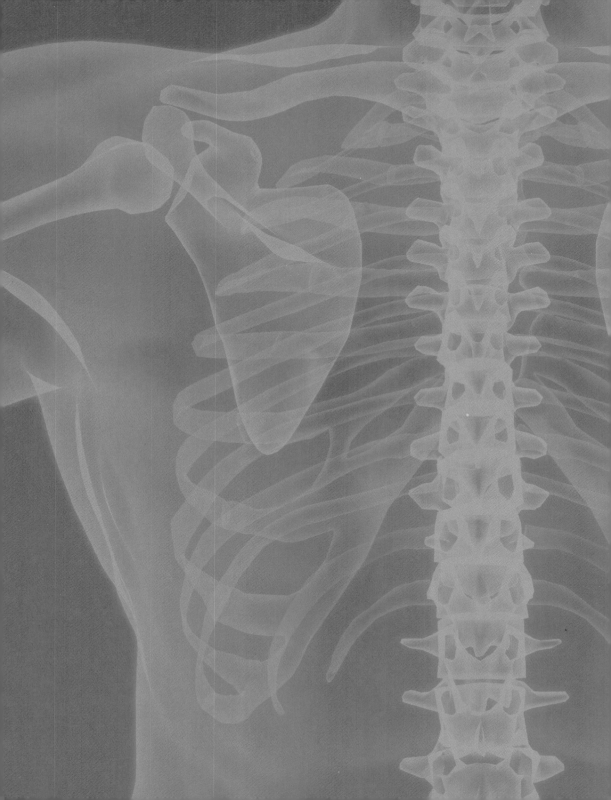

Chapter **10** – *Running*

'Our muscular mechanisms were elaborated by nature over a thousand million years not to be the types of static painful machines into which society and its machines have so far transformed the vast majority of them. They were built up against the forces of gravity specifically to make us capable of such perfection in balancing as to float as it were in space over the surface of the Earth, joyfully, painlessly'

Raymond Dart

'Unlike swimmers, golfers, and tennis players, few runners today are taught running form in part because of a common assumption that running, like walking, is so natural that all humans develop a natural form appropriate to their anatomy and physiology'

Daniel Lieberman

Running to live

In recent years researchers in biology, palaeoanthropology and evolutionary medicine have become increasingly convinced that running – often at speed for sustained periods using aerobic metabolism – has played a hugely important part in changing human anatomy over the past two million years. 'We think of walking as the quintessential human gait, and it is,' says Daniel Lieberman, but 'the human body is also loaded with features that make us really exceptional runners. Our gifts and our ability to run are not just a by-product of walking, but its own special skill that we have'.

That cluster of novel anatomical and physiological features allowing us to run long distances with a spring in the step differentiates us from our closest relatives, such as bonobos, chimpanzees and gorillas. These African apes can run on two legs, often at great speed, but only over very short distances. Apart from the proliferation of sweat glands and absence of body fur, allowing the loss of excess body heat through evaporation rather than through panting, the unique set of human characteristics includes an external nose which allows incoming air to be heated and humidified and the nuchal ligament, a fibrous membrane attached to the bony protuberance at the base of the skull, which runs to the base of the neck and keeps the head still. We also possess long legs with inward-sloping thigh bones; large knee joints and powerful muscles replete with red muscle fibres; long Achilles tendons and plantar arches on the underside of the feet which work as elastic springs allowing the storage and release of energy; and an enlarged gluteus maximus, a powerful extensor muscle, which connects the thigh bones to the trunk and acts to stabilise the torso when leaning forward and moving at speed.

But why are we capable of running? The best guess is that between two and three million years ago the African continent once again experienced a period of significant cooling with the result that the supply of plant food diminished. Over time strong selection ensured that our bipedal walking, ape-like ancestors lost their small, stocky statures so useful in climbing trees for food and shelter, and developed tall, lithe physiques capable of running long distances in open grasslands to scavenge carcasses and later on

Above San hunter drinking water from an ostrich egg

to wear down prey through heat exhaustion – so-called persistence hunting. That bestowed a competitive advantage over other mammals seeking the same food sources. The energy-rich, high-protein high-fat diet led to the evolution of smaller stomachs but very large brains. In turn this transformation in diet made trotting and running hominins smarter and better able to collaborate and co-operate. In a nutshell, our ancestors ran to eat but in doing so greatly improved their chances of survival and reproductive success and so changed the course of history. Running is one of the important factors for more than seven billion anatomically and culturally complex humans being alive today.

Above San hunters

The number of populations practising persistence hunting has dwindled enormously over the course of the last few centuries. In recent years one of the few known groups of foragers carrying on the tradition are a small number of San people in the arid, sparsely vegetated central Kalahari in southern Africa. Three or four men will drink as much water as they can and then chase down antelopes, wild cats or other animals at the hottest time of the day in temperatures that average between 39° and 42°C. The hunters maintain speeds of around four to six miles an hour, covering up to 22 miles until their job is done.

Other hunter-gatherers such as the Hadza do not go in for persistence hunting. Instead Hadza men use a variety of different strategies to find high-quality game, including scavenging. When animals such as buffalo, impala and zebra are killed by leopards, lions or hyenas, Hadza hunters are quick to observe the vultures often circling overhead. They will run at speed and chase away animals feeding on the carcass by firing arrows and shouting and then consume or bring back to camp what remains. They also run as they hunt and track prey.

Above A Hadza man with bow and arrow

Running as recreation

Although people of all cultures run when they have to (perhaps you have experience of running for a bus or train, or hurrying to a meeting), in our society running is also a popular recreational pastime. It's something that many of us do because we believe it promotes fitness and well-being. Running is the second most accessible form of exercise available after walking. It can be done anywhere – in the city, in the country, or at the beach – with the minimum

Above Two people running

amount of equipment by anyone who is reasonably healthy. In the US it is estimated that the number of regular runners has increased from four to 14 million people in the last decade. In the UK around two million people spend at least 30 minutes a week running or jogging, up by a third from 2005.

Running as a business

Running has become big business. Consider the numerous marathons held in major cities, the half marathons held in smaller cities and the charity races held in all sorts of places worldwide which raise so much money for good causes. And of course running as part of elite track and field, cross-country and road-running, is a global spectator sport, viewed not only by those watching live but also on screens in living rooms, gyms and sports clubs, as well as on mobile devices.

Consider also the number of factory workers working flat out to produce innovative running shoes, clothing, and accessories for affluent consumers. The profits for the companies that own global brands are huge. And some of that money in the form of lucrative endorsements and sponsorships is bestowed on athletes who compete at the highest level. For several months of the year these competitors live in hotel rooms and rented accommodation and forgo what most of us would consider a normal life, doing little else but training, eating, and sleeping all the while dreaming of success, and the diverse benefits that sporting superstardom will bring.

The popularity of running

Why is running is such a popular pastime? There are many reasons, of course. But observe any primary school playground at break anywhere in the world and children will be running about, chasing one another laughing and shouting as they do so.

Above Modern running shoes make it more likely that a runner will heel strike and pull the head back and down, though running barefoot may or may not help

Whatever its evolutionary origins the lesson we learn from young children is that running, especially outdoors really is good fun. At an individual level the activity is a natural progression from lying in supine, then turning over to crawl on all fours, through the first tottering steps in upright balance and then into walking. For children running is an important part of physical and social development. And the laughter accompanying their play gives a clue about why many adults enjoy the activity. Apart from setting and achieving goals, running in a coordinated way even at a relatively moderate pace can put a smile on people's faces.

However when I observe adult joggers and runners on roads and footpaths and in parks it is apparent that for the vast majority it is all a bit of a slog. Rather than detecting a smile I am more likely to see a frown or a grimace. In contrast to habitually barefoot (or minimally shod) east Africans (and others) who move gracefully with a spring in their step, most of us either shuffle along or pound the ground looking as if our heads are too heavy to carry. Putting modern running shoes on our feet often causes problems as cushioned, elevated heels and arch supports encourage most of us to stiffen our ankles, slam down our feet and over stride (the ankle lands in advance of the knee). In turn that makes us fix our knee and hip joints, which also adversely affects the balance of our heads on our necks. Intriguingly, compared with running barefoot, running with cushioned shoes increases heart rate, which suggests that more energy is being expended. Cushioned shoes reduce significantly the amount of proprioceptive information coming from the soles of the feet. Runners should reflect on the fact that for most of human evolutionary history people ran either barefoot or with thin-soled sandals or moccasins. Perhaps we should stick to those options.

That said running barefoot or using minimalist shoes will not solve the problem of malcoordination if it has become established in the body-mind. Furthermore although a badly coordinated jogger or runner may well get some of the benefits of aerobic exercise – the post-exercise glow and positive feelings, even euphoria, triggered by the release of endorphins – there will also be a significant degree of compression throughout the body, signalled by the head being pulled down on to the neck.

That's a high price to pay. In the long-term any pattern of biomechanically inefficient running will almost inevitably lead to painful joint and muscle problems. Those include anything from Achilles tendonitis and patellofemoral pain syndrome, so-called runner's knee, to bunions and stress fractures of the heel and shin bones. Indeed studies suggest that between 30 and 80 per cent of runners in the developed world incur running-related injuries each year. Interestingly one of the most common is lower back pain, a condition unheard of amongst contemporary hunter-gatherers. Rest, compression bandages and ice packs will often work wonders for minor injuries, but sometimes surgical intervention, including bone grafts, hip and knee replacements, is required to sort out the more serious long-term problems.

Running fast badly

Michael Johnson

Some champion athletes do not run with fantastic coordination. Texan-born Michael Johnson, winner of four Olympic gold medals in the 200 metres and 400 metres in the individual and relay events, who remains the current 300 metres and 400 metres world record holder, had a highly idiosyncratic way of running. Even as a child he moved in a very stiff-backed way with an almost military-style bearing, using short, choppy steps. His friends used to say, 'You run funny'

to which Johnson's answer was, 'well, you run slow.' Later, when he started to compete in international competitions, some media commentators also queried aspects of his running style. The reply from the man famous for wearing golden spikes was more or less the same as he delivered to his one-time playmates: 'I can run faster than you can.'

Apart from the stiff, over-straightened back, what Johnson's critics often failed to notice however was the way he rocked from side to side as he ran, not only as he negotiated the bends of the running track but also in the home straight. That was inefficient and a waste of the great Olympian's energy. After retirement Johnson tellingly said: 'I always knew that I could run faster than I ran.'

Left Michael Johnson running with his head pulled down on to his neck, lifting his chest and pulling in his lower back

Usain Bolt

The already legendary gold Olympian Usain Bolt stands at 1.96m (6' 5"). When running flat out in competition he has a loping gait, contorts his face, hunches his shoulders, and rolls from side to side, albeit in a manner different from Michael Johnson. Significantly the Jamaican athlete, the world record holder at 100 metres and 200 metres, was born with a sideways curvature of the spine known as scoliosis.

As a teenager performing sprints Bolt experienced distressing lower back problems because of his condition. Nowadays in order to manage his problem he is always accompanied by a masseuse, whose job it is to knead the muscles before and after his daily training schedule, as well as after racing. So that his scoliosis can be closely monitored Bolt flies to Germany two or three times a year to consult some of the world's top specialists in sports medicine. Like many other people, Bolt has a structural condition which affects his general coordination. However it is also true to say that his general coordination will interact with and affect his structural condition.

It's interesting though how much more efficiently Bolt runs when he is so far out in front of his competitors in the latter part of a 100 or 200 metres race that he feels that he can 'relax' and take a look around. His neck muscles let go, his head goes forward and up, and the rocking from side to side diminishes. So why is Bolt unable to perform like that all the time? The answer is that like the rest of us he is a prisoner of his kinaesthetic sense. Bolt most likely feels that he has to run in his habitual way in order to generate the power and speed that has won him so many races.

Although many might find it hard to believe the truth is that Bolt, the fastest man in history who has touched speeds of 27.9 mph, could run more quickly if he tried less hard. Of course it is often difficult for a full-time athlete to change a running style because of habit, especially one that is continually reinforced by so much repetitive training.

Bolt could perhaps take a few things from the Alexander Technique. Firstly, he needs to learn how to allow the column of his neck to lengthen out of the trunk with the head poised on top of the spine. Secondly, rather than pull up his shoulders towards the neck they should be allowed to remain as part of the back. Finally, Bolt should think of leaning up and forward from the pivot point of the ankle joints to prevent any side-to-side movement. We will explore this in more detail later.

Above Usain Bolt using too much effort (left) but running much more efficiently once victory has been secured (right)

Running fast brilliantly

Tirunesh Dibaba

Conversely there are some athletes who really are very well coordinated. One of the best contemporary examples is Tirunesh Dibaba, an Olympic gold medallist on the track and the first woman to retain the 10,000 metres in successive Olympics in 2008 and 2012. She is also the holder of World Championship titles and winner of multiple World Cross Country Championships. Little wonder that in many people's eyes she is the most technically-gifted distance runner, male or female, of all time.

The daughter of subsistence farmers, Dibaba, who stands at 1.62m (5'3"), hails from the village of Bekoji, which lies more than 9000 feet above sea level in Ethiopia's southern highlands about 170 miles from the capital, Addis Ababa. A skinny kid, who no one thought had any chance of success when she first started training at the age of 14, Dibaba overturned that perception four years later in 2003 when she won the World Championship 5000 metres title in Paris. That victory led to her being nicknamed the 'baby-faced assassin', because of her facial features and her ability to destroy opponents, including her compatriots, with a blistering finish. She is so fast over the final lap (her best time in a race is 58.33 seconds in 2005) that some commentators have even suggested that Dibaba had the makings of a world-class 400 metres runner.

Above Ethiopia's Tirunesh Dibaba leading the way with her head freely poised on top of her spine

Tirunesh Dibaba's running style

We can learn a lot by observing those who are really well coordinated and working out how they perform an activity. So the obvious question is: what distinguishes Tirunesh Dibaba from her competitors? Basically, it is the fluidity of her running style – she runs as if she is floating over the track. For Dibaba running is part of a total neuromuscular pattern, but if broken down there are a number of features that characterise her movement. She possesses a particularly well connected primary control with the neck and head lengthening out of a supportive back, and the shoulders releasing into width. Her head remains balanced on the top of the spine, even when she looks behind or up at stadium screens to monitor what her competitors are doing. She is remarkably symmetrical. When running she provides a spectacular demonstration of the efficiency of the body's spiral mechanism in action, with just the right amount but not too much rotation in the neck and trunk. Her pelvis remains on a level plane. Her arms release away efficiently from the chest wall, opening and closing around a 90 degree angle at the elbows, using a fluid backward-forward motion.

Above Tirunesh Dibaba demonstrating the importance of the body's spiral mechanism

As her arms swing forward alternately, the hands rise to the vertical midpoint at the top of her chest. Unless she is sprinting her elbows do not reach forward beyond her torso. She also keeps her wrists flat, with the fingers and thumbs releasing into length.

Looking at Dibaba's movement in the lower limbs there are five additional characteristics. Firstly, the way her whole body releases up and forward from the pivot point of the ankle joints. Secondly, because she enjoys such good support from her back musculature, her legs elastically release forward from a contra-rotating torso. In turn that allows an equality of both inward and outward spiralling of the thighs, with neither rotation overpowering the other irrespective of whether the feet are hanging in the air or in contact with the ground. Thirdly, as she lands on the ball of the front foot, her leg moves quickly rearwards so that when she takes off from the big toe it is positioned directly under the vertical midline of her torso. Fourthly, at the end of the rearward leg phase her heels almost touch her sitting bones – even at the end of a gruelling 10,000 metres race or half marathon – clearly demonstrating the efficiency of her overall movement. Finally, when Dibaba produces her trademark kick in the final stage of a race, there is no obvious change of gears. She accelerates smoothly and efficiently, arms and legs working in perfect synchronicity, without any sign of exertion or strain in her face, or in her breathing. Truly watching Tirunesh Dibaba run is to see poetry in motion.

Clearly not everyone can run that fast and with that degree of coordination. Dibaba evidently possesses factor X. Nevertheless everyone who has the capacity to run can greatly improve their running style if they put their body-mind to it and if they know what they need to do, and not do, in order to improve.

New ways of running

So the relevant question from an Alexander Technique perspective is: if you wish to run what is the most efficient way to do so? I'm sure you now know that like any other activity running efficiently involves allowing your neck to release so that your head is free to move forward and up in such a way that your back lengthens and widens and your limbs release out of the trunk before you move and as you move. Easy to say of course, not so easy to carry out.

The big error most of us make in the transition from walking into running is to over stride. The reason that happens, I suggest, is linked to the commonsense perception that achieving a good distance between the feet is synonymous with running. Simply put, walking uses short strides and running uses

Above Jumping or hopping into running

long strides, so it is best to achieve a long stride as quickly as possible. To that end most joggers and runners hop or jump, as it were, into the run pulling their heads down on to their necks as they do so. This pattern of running, despite being used by some world-class athletes, is inefficient and a waste of effort. Moreover much evidence suggests that it can cause injuries of one sort or another. There are far better ways to get started. I will show you two.

Using micro-steps

I will ask you to look out, inhibit and direct and stand either with both feet underneath your head, or one behind the other, your heels a few inches apart with the toes turned out slightly. If you are standing with too much weight on the front of your feet this needs to be corrected. So give the directions for the primary control and allow yourself to come slightly back from the ankles so that you achieve a good heel contact, toes releasing forward. At all times resist any urge to actively lean forward in the direction you want to run, which will make you lose height. Instead think of an upward release through your ankles, knees and hips. The release in your legs will reinforce the direction up along the spine towards the crown of your freely poised head which is going skyward. At this point, while maintaining contact with your heels, simply *think* of leaning up and forward from the pivot point of the ankle joints as if you were about to go up on to your toes.

Above Floating over the surface of the Earth

Now start the movement by allowing your head to release over your feet, or if the feet are in the fore-aft position from over your back foot to the front foot. In either case that will result in a forward transfer of weight which will take you into balanced walking. Do not be in a hurry; move quite slowly keeping your internal length. As you walk, maintain your directions and then make a decision to progressively shorten your stride. You will end up taking smaller and smaller steps – micro steps, as it were, resulting in a rapid increase in foot pickup. Now you are falling upwards and forwards, the contra-rotations around the spinal axis activated, your legs releasing forward and rearward with your heels moving in an arc toward the sitting bones. In addition allow your arms, with the elbows now bent at around 90 degrees to move in a rhythmic backward-forward motion.

As your speed increases through the up and forward release from your ankles, your stride will automatically lengthen to counterbalance the working of the double spiral musculature in the torso. Add on a direction for your shoulders to release away from each other. Depending perhaps on how fast you are moving either your midfoot or forefoot, but *not* your heel, will land underneath your head. If you want to move faster, there is no need to do anything directly with your legs. You simply give a direction to increase the degree of up and forward lean from your ankles while maintaining the balance of your head on your neck, and your legs and arms will respond appropriately. Also, by keeping your ankles released your feet will adjust automatically to the terrain on which you are moving. You can keep running for as long as is comfortable, or until you get tired.

Starting your run

Look out and see something

Inhibit and give the directions for the primary control

Think of an upward release through your ankles, knees and hips

Think of leaning up and forward from your ankles while maintaining your heel contact

Allow your head to release forward over the feet to take you into walking

Consciously shorten your stride so that you take micro-steps, progressively falling up and forward, your feet landing underneath your head and then releasing rearwards in an arc towards your sitting bones

Allow the contra-rotations in your torso to work without 'doing' them

Over the first few strides let your arms assume a 90 degree angle around the elbow joints, and move in a rhythmic backward-forward movement

Your speed will be determined in large part by the degree of up and forward lean from your ankles working in conjunction with your freely poised head

---

Running backwards

The second way of exploring running is to run backwards for a short distance. (If you are not familiar with barefoot running but would like to experiment with it then this is an ideal opportunity to remove your shoes because you will not be running very far.) Look out and stand with your feet underneath your freely poised head with your toes turned out slightly. Alternatively start the process with one foot behind the other with most of your weight supported by the rear leg. Inhibit and direct and then if necessary come back a fraction from your ankles so that your whole body is releasing up and back counterbalanced by your head going forwards and up. The result should be that you now have a good contact with the ground. Allow your arms to form right angles without stiffening at the elbow joints.

Now order an extra release up and back from your ankle joints and then allow, say, your left knee to release forward and away so that the left foot peels off the ground, the ball of your foot landing underneath your backward moving trunk. As your weight moves into the heel of that rearward foot, the heel of your right foot starts to peel off the ground, and you will find that you are slowly walking backwards. Be careful not to over stride. Additionally your arms should be allowed to move freely taking their cue from the contra-rotation of your shoulders in opposition to the pelvis. Keep the upward direction along the spine and maintain the free poise of your head. Stay in balance and begin to take micro steps.

Above A group of children experiment with running backwards

You can now allow an increase in the speed at which you are picking up your feet. Very soon you will be running, landing on the forefoot. You can experiment employing a slow, medium or fast pace – your stride will automatically lengthen the faster you run – but make sure that you do not bump into anything! When you decide that it is appropriate, maintain the release in your neck, inhibit and then let your eyes look either to your left or right shoulder and then behind you while allowing, in sequence, your head, upper and then lower torso, followed by your legs and feet to turn. You are now running in a forward direction.

That experience will provide an insight into how your body's spiral mechanism can work to your advantage. Indeed many runners using the Alexander Technique also find that running backwards gives them an invaluable experience of the direction of the contra-rotating spine going 'up and back' which they can then take into running forward. This might sound like a paradox, but it isn't!

Using the lunge in racing

Lunging is another basic human movement. It's often used – sometimes well, sometimes not so well – by runners at all distances from 800 metres upwards. Well-coordinated runners never stand with their feet side by side, but instead walk or jog to the start line, place one foot behind the other and then lean up and forward from the hip and ankle joints. Some such as Tirunesh Dibaba and Kenya's David Rudisha, the current 800 metres world record holder and the 2012 Olympic champion, perform the movement very efficiently – that is they bend at the ankles, knees and hips while maintaining internal length – but others tighten and pull down. That's definitely not the way to start a competitive race as the resulting compression of the head, neck and back loads body weight on to the legs, acting as a brake on momentum. Unless there is some conscious intervention by an athlete that pattern will last throughout the race.

So what is the way of starting a race with good use? Stand at the start line with your feet underneath your head, inhibit and give your orders for the primary control. Then without pressing down place one foot a little way behind you, with the toes turned out slightly. Ensure that you maintain a good heel contact with both feet. At this point most of your weight will be supported by your rear leg. Now inhibit and direct and bend your knees so that they release over the toes. You can then pivot forward from your hip joints. A shallow bend is all that is required.

Above 800 m Olympic Champion David Rudisha of Kenya demonstrating that the eyes lead and the body follows

Although some athletes allow their arms to dangle out of the back at a start of a race, from a momentum point of view it is better that the upper limbs are used well from the outset in order to optimally engage the double spiral musculature. For example, if you are standing with your left foot forward your right shoulder and arm should be forward, while the left arm will be behind your torso. Both arms will be bent, roughly at right angles at the elbow.

You can now allow your head to release forward over the left foot while maintaining a heel contact with both feet. That shift in body weight will create a stretch from your feet to your head. You are at a tipping point, poised to move. You can begin running either through your own decision, or if you are in a race, at the sound of the starting pistol. In either case, allow an extra forward release of your head over the left foot, while directing your left knee to release forward from the hip joint and middle back at the same time as your right elbow releases backwards in space. You will be running in monkey. Be careful not to over stride or come up too quickly. If you observe well-coordinated world-class middle and long-distance runners you will see that they are running in a shallow monkey for at least 15 strides, slowly coming to upright, keeping the back open and the head balanced. You should follow their example.

The upper body in running

The shoulders and arms

As with walking many of us also find in running that there is an almost irresistible temptation to hunch the shoulders. That habit comes at a high price since lifting the shoulders uses the same muscles as those involved in tightening the neck. To avoid this you can think of the directions required when you place your hands over the back of a chair. Ensure that your shoulder blades lie flat on your rib cage as you think of widening the upper part of your arms (and shoulder girdle) and your back. This will engage your body's anti-gravity musculature.

In running the arms as well as stabilising the torso play a dynamic role in generating momentum. When your arm, with the elbow at around 90 degrees, moves forward towards the midpoint of your torso, it is a reflex action – the fingers of one hand will lead forward without effort because of the backward direction of the opposite elbow and shoulder. For that reason you need to be aware that if you actively push your arms and hands forward, instead of allowing them to release forward, you will be working against yourself and lose speed.

In order to achieve optimum movement and momentum your hands should not cross the twisting vertical axis of your spine. If you do this it will affect your legs and feet creating an inefficient, swinging side-to-side motion. The chances are that it will also cause you to over stride.

Fingers and thumbs

Many running coaches advocate that the hands should be held in a loose fist with the thumb placed on the first crease of the forefinger (index finger) using a light touch as if you were holding a butterfly. It's certainly an effective way of monitoring what you are doing with the hands. However I think it is unnecessarily restrictive. In fact there are plenty of ways of organising your lengthening hands and fingers that do not create tension so you should feel free to experiment.

Nevertheless there's no doubt that what you do with your thumbs is very important in the effect it has on your running style. Stiffening these digits will inevitably create tension in your flexor muscles, such as those around your elbow and the inside of the upper arm. Stiff thumbs will also have serious consequences in the way in which your legs move, as the required support from the anti-gravity musculature of the back will be interfered with. Your legs will then be forced to do too much work and lose springiness. The feet, including your big toes, will also stiffen. In a nutshell, your thumbs should be directed to release into length at all times.

Stretching

Exercise physiologists are divided about the benefits of stretching both before and after running. Some think it is useful, while others think that static stretching, such as touching the toes and holding that position, is harmful because it loosens muscles and tendons contributing to a loss of elasticity, flexibility and strength. The latter viewpoint perhaps explains why the practice has declined dramatically amongst elite athletes in recent years.

Above Static stretching with the head pulled back results in compression throughout the body

On the other hand all sport scientists recommend warming up the muscles and gradually increasing the heart rate and body temperature, for example by performing a brisk walk or light jog for five to ten minutes before beginning more strenuous activity, as well as cooling down at the end of training to prevent blood pooling in the lower body. It's very sensible advice.

From an Alexander Technique perspective moving around in a constant gravitational field while maintaining lengthening of the stature creates a dynamic and constant stretch throughout your body. There is no real reason unless there is local tightness, say in your hamstrings or calves to perform specific stretching exercises before or after running. It's all too evident that the way in which many runners stretch actually creates unnecessary tension in their bodies. Take for example the widespread practice of a runner standing in a lunge, one leg behind the other with open hands placed against a wall or tree. The body weight is then brought forward to stretch the leg muscles. But observe most people when they perform this action and you will see that they displace the pelvis forward, pull the lower back in, and lift the rear heel. In short, it actively prevents the right kind of stretch in the calves and hamstring muscles, which play such a crucial role in running.

A better way to stretch

A much better way of performing the procedure is to inhibit and direct and then perform a lunge, with your back leg straight but not braced back and your front leg bent so that the knee is releasing over your toes. Then with open hands allow the palms followed by your slightly-spread fingers to make contact with a wall or tree at shoulder height. You will realise, I hope, that you are following more or less the same process as you learnt for placing hands on the table in monkey which is covered in Chapter 7. Now all you have to do is think your hands and your feet to release into the contact surfaces – the wall and the ground – as you maintain

Above A poor post-running stretch, pulling the head back and down, and pulling the back in

Above Using the knuckles to stretch effectively

your directions to the neck, head and back, while ordering your back up and back. There is no need to 'do' anything. Instead you are consciously directing, which will indirectly activate the appropriate stretch reflexes in the musculature.

However if you find that you are collapsing on to the palms of your hands – that is, your head, neck and trunk are moving or pressing towards your hands rather than releasing away from them – you might find it more effective to use the two largest knuckles of each hand. In that way you will get more support, reducing the risk of collapsing or pulling down.

Playful running

There are other things to experiment with in running. For example, unlike young children running around a playground or other open space nearly all adult runners tend to run in straight lines. The next time you visit the running track, park or beach try running in a zigzag

Above We can learn a lot by observing children running and having fun

pattern or in circles for a change, or add these movements to your warm-up and cool-down phases. If you are able to it is a good idea to also perform a brief session of Alexander lying down before, or after, running (or both) to get yourself into better shape.

The running revolution

The running revolution did not really start in the West until the 1960s and 70s when it was popularised by journalist Jim Fixx and cardiologist Dr George Sheehan. It's thus not surprising that running is not a topic given extensive coverage in any of Alexander's books, which were published between 1910 and 1941. Nevertheless we do have his opinion in the first edition of his first book, *Man's Supreme Inheritance*, concerning the legendary Dorando Pietri's running action in the closing stages of the 1908 London Olympic Marathon.

Above Dorando Pietri at the finish line of the London Olympics 1908 Marathon

Despite collapsing five times after entering the White City Stadium, the Italian runner, a pastry chef by trade, went on to win the 26 miles 385 yards race in 2:54:46 (considerably slower than the current world record of 2:02:57 set by Kenya's Dennis Kimetto in Berlin in 2014.) There was a sting in the tail, however. Pietri was disqualified because of the help he had received from officials anxious to avoid him dying in the presence of Queen Alexandra, Queen-Empress consort of Edward VII, who was observing his ordeal from the Royal Box.

Not surprisingly an official objection was lodged after the conclusion of the race. The gold medal was subsequently awarded to the second-placed athlete, the American Johnny Hayes, who had been timed 30 seconds behind the winner. Inevitably the amended result caused great controversy. Sir Arthur Conan Doyle, the Scottish physician and author, who was at the finish, was so hugely impressed by Pietri's determination to win that he later wrote: 'Amid stooping figures and grasping hands I caught a glimpse of the haggard, yellow face, the glazed, expressionless eyes, the long, black hair streaked across the brow… The Italian's great performance can never be effaced from our record of sport, be the decision of the judges what it may.'

Alexander, who was not present but relied on press reports, took a very different view of Pietri's efforts. 'One sees that he was desperately weary, and that whatever conscious control of his muscular mechanisms he may ever have obtained, he was at this moment completely under the domination of subconscious (or subjective control), that he was out of "communication with his reason",' he noted. 'His body, as we see him in these photographs is thrown back from the hips, his arms outstretched behind him and his legs bent forward at the knee. As a consequence, he is compelled to use almost all his physical force in order to save himself from falling backwards. He is struggling against a tremendous gravitational pull which is dragging him away from his goal.'

Although Pietri was clearly in a state of exhaustion – it is possible he was suffering from the debilitating effects of dehydration as the race was held on a hot and humid July day – Alexander suggested that if the 'magnificent athlete' had been trained in the basics of his technique, he would have employed his 'commonsense' and 'leaned forward not back and while he had the strength necessary (but a very small part of the strength he was actually expending) to prevent himself from falling on his face, that gravitational force would dragged him on instead of dragging him back from the object of his achievement. He would, in short, have been able to make the *best* instead of the *worst* of his powers.'

Alexander's point is well made. In fact watch any number of contemporary top-class athletes as they approach the finish line in both sprints and distance races and you will observe that a significant proportion of them are leaning back, chins tilted upward and losing height, either because they feel tired or because they are overly worried about what the opposition are up to and are trying too hard.

> **Things to think about when running**
>
> *Stay in the moment and take in the environment by using your eyes and ears*
>
> *Pay particular attention to the balance of your head on the neck*
>
> *Maintain the thought of leaning up and forward from the pivot point of the ankles*
>
> *Allow the contra-rotations in your torso to work*
>
> *Avoid over striding and heel striking*
>
> *Do not lock your knees at any point in the running cycle*
>
> *Do not stick your arms out – the elbows should release and open towards the ground*
>
> *Maintain freedom in your wrists*
>
> *Direct your thumbs to release into length*

So Alexander's recommendation about learning an efficient way of running utilising gravity – even when extreme fatigue has set in – is still as relevant today for elite runners as it was for Pietri in 1908. And that lesson has a wider application, whether you are a club runner, jogger, or an occasional fun runner, particularly in preventing injuries of one sort or another.

The Alexander Technique holds out the tantalising possibility that runners of all levels (including those of us running for buses) would value the activity more highly if it could be performed with greater fluidity of movement. Indeed even elite runners, who have minor or major deficiencies in their running style and are prepared to take the time to learn to move with greater efficiency, could run faster.

Running the Alexander way requires maintaining the balance of the head on the spine and keeping better general coordination, by thinking in activity even when that activity is fast-moving. Then if the conditions are right – having sufficient energy and being well-hydrated are obviously both very important factors – your body's machinery, the result of millions of years of evolution, will carry out your intention to move at speed. It's as simple as that!

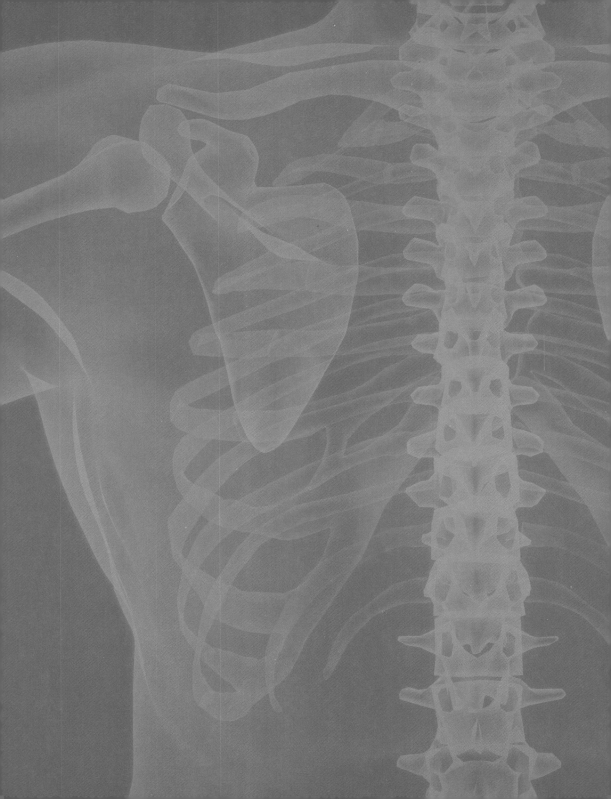

Chapter **11** – *Questions & Answers*

In this concluding section of the book, I have attempted
to answer some of the questions I am often asked
by new and experienced students

I first came for lessons in the Alexander Technique to sort out my 'posture'. I now realise it is about thinking and movement. Why do you think the technique has become synonymous with the term posture?

That's a very good question. Over the last few centuries in Western and Western-influenced societies practices emanating from the aristocracy, as well as the military, have been highly influential in defining and shaping concepts of what makes for 'good' and 'bad' posture. You can see these, now deeply-held cultural assumptions, being played out on popular television programmes such as the UK's *Strictly Come Dancing* and its US equivalent *Dancing with the Stars*. The judges, especially those keen to uphold the various traditions of ballroom dancing, will often reprimand contestants for not having the appropriate look. 'Your posture really needs to be worked on,' they say. 'Remember to keep your head up, lift your chest (or diaphragm) and keep your shoulders back.'

Unfortunately that kind of instruction only encourages people to stiffen, lose height and interfere with their breathing. A much better tip for contestants would be to look at videos of Fred Astaire and his partners, especially Ginger Rogers, Rita Hayworth and Barrie Chase and try to work out how they moved while maintaining an effortless-looking light-footedness.

I think that the concept of 'good' and 'bad' posture has also become increasingly influential because of the use of the chair in work, education, leisure and the home. 'Sit up straight' is a phrase uttered innumerable times by exasperated parents, who see their children slouching at the dining table, or in front of the television or the computer, using a notion that collapsing is 'bad' but sitting upright – alas, any sort of upright – is 'good'. Because sitting is a relatively static movement we often do not appreciate that what's going on inside the body is incredibly dynamic. We tend to think of sitting in an overly simplistic way – so 'good' posture is a shape that has to be actively 'done' and then strenuously and heroically maintained through hard work.

I suspect that in part the Alexander Technique has become synonymous with 'good' posture because of the importance given to getting in and out of the chair. It's easy for a new student or outside observers to look at what's going on in a lesson and think, 'Aha! This is about posture because it is about sitting', even though it is very far removed from that. Certainly editors at

Above Fred Astaire (1899-1987) dancing with his sister Adele (1896-1981)

mainstream publishing companies haven't helped. If you look at the titles of popular books on the Alexander Technique you will find a significant proportion have 'posture' either in the title or in the subtitle.

We know from his writings and occasional public lectures that FM Alexander had little time for the term 'posture', simply because it comes with so much cultural baggage, so many multiple, often contradictory, meanings. It's time we all gave up thinking of the Alexander Technique as something that sorts out 'bad' posture and instead start to think of it as the founder intended – improving general coordination or poise in almost any activity through creative thinking.

I've heard that some people continue to have on-going lessons. Why is that?

Well, professional and semi-professional performers – musicians, dancers and actors, for instance – are often very enthusiastic about the Alexander Technique because they know very well that the use of their bodies is central not only to their health and well-being but also to how they make a living. After their initial course of lessons, often provided as part of the college curriculum, many performers will carry on having regular lessons and notably before a major performance.

Another group of people deriving on-going benefit from the Alexander Technique are those who choose to have lessons for what might be termed 'lifestyle' reasons. Some of my longest-standing students work in the financial services sector in the City of London. They say that lessons not only help them maintain a sense of well-being – a very useful counterbalance to the pressures and stresses involved in carrying out transactions in the dealing room – but they also enjoy learning about inhibition, direction and movement as applied to different aspects of their lives, especially pastimes such as walking, running, cycling, football, golf or swimming.

But whatever your motivation it is important that you receive an intensive course of Alexander lessons from a qualified and skilled teacher, who has undergone a three year full-time training at an approved institution. In the UK the oldest and largest organisation is the Society of Teachers of the Alexander Technique (STAT), the institution to which I belong.

How many Alexander lessons do I need?

The answer depends on your problem, your interests and your goals. Teachers of the Alexander Technique often use a rule of thumb that 30 lessons is a good starting point. The reason for that number is that when Alexander gave his students an introductory course of half-hour lessons, they came every weekday (and sometimes on Saturdays as well) for six weeks. On the other hand Alexander, very wisely, was careful not to prejudge a situation. In fact he never gave a prospective student an exact number of lessons. Instead he used to say, 'We'll have to work and see. To a certain extent it is up to you how deeply you want to go into it.' I give the same advice. Of course in learning the technique a lot depends on the kinaesthetic intelligence and application of a student. Some people have good awareness of their body, some do not; some are keen to learn, some are not.

But let's say that you have niggling neck, shoulder or lower back pain. Assuming that the condition is functional – that is, it's caused by something you are doing to yourself in everyday life – then, if you can learn not to tighten and contract so much of the time, it won't be so much of an issue and might even disappear completely. The major study of the effects of Alexander lessons on chronic lower back pain carried out by medical researchers at the universities of Bristol and Southampton, published as the cover story in the *British Medical Journal* on 19 August 2008, found very significant effects from as few as six lessons, although 24 lessons gave better results in terms of pain reduction and overall mobility measured over a 12-month period.

I have never met anyone who has had a course of Alexander lessons without having some sort of problem to solve. Moreover the range of problems is extremely varied – office workers aiming to correct 'bad' posture and alleviate back, neck and shoulder pain; people recovering from accidents and surgery; musicians whose malcoordination is getting in the way of playing their chosen instrument; singers who have reached the end of their tether because their voice has become strained; the exercise-minded who want to learn how to run rather than jog inefficiently; young dancers who wish to improve their performance; older dancers, who after a lifetime of misusing themselves, have problems with their feet, ankles and knees, and so on.

There are also those who come to the technique suffering from a variety of hard-to-treat conditions such as anxiety, chronic fatigue syndrome, depression, IBS, migraine, and various rheumatic and inflammatory disorders. The list goes on. Obviously poor coordination, while not causal, can certainly add to the burden of suffering, and learning improved coordination can reduce it.

Will the Alexander Technique cure my chronic back pain?

Although the technique is not a treatment or therapy your back pain might well be ameliorated, or even disappear, if you have lessons. That might seem paradoxical. Let me explain. The technique is concerned with prevention rather than cure. Although the precise cause of chronic back pain is often difficult to pinpoint, it is usually related to conditions such as a herniated disc – the so-called slipped disc – and by a variety of inflammatory processes in the musculoskeletal system, as well as age-related degeneration, especially in those over 65. Lower back pain has also been linked to anxiety and stress. Nevertheless whatever the cause if you are willing to take the time to learn to stop shortening in stature, even to some extent, this may well stop or at least diminish the pain originating in your muscles, tendons, ligaments, nerves or bones and create the conditions for repair. But it's very important that you get an accurate medical diagnosis in order to rule out firstly, that you do not have a pathological anatomical problem of the spine, such as a fracture, and secondly, that you're not suffering from conditions such as bacterial or fungal infections, kidney stones, malignancy, or the effects of long-term corticosteroid use, all of which can masquerade as chronic or acute functional back pain.

Is the Alexander Technique available on the NHS?

Although at the moment the Alexander Technique is only recommended by the UK's National Institute for Health and Clinical Excellence (NICE) in its 'exercise' category, some GPs do prescribe lessons for the management of back pain. Furthermore a small number of Alexander Technique teachers currently work in pain clinics in a few NHS hospitals. The availability of lessons provided by various NHS agencies might well change when the results of on-going scientific research into the effects of the technique on a variety of conditions, including chronic neck pain, becomes available. In the meantime you will find that some private health insurance schemes in the UK, US, Australia and other countries will fund a course of lessons in the Alexander Technique if it is recommended by a qualified medical practitioner.

You once quoted Alexander, 'We need to change the people not the furniture.' Can you explain further?

It's a memorable phrase, isn't it? Alexander was highlighting something of great importance. He was making the point that if you possess a reasonable degree of conscious general coordination it should make it possible for you to adapt to all manner of different-shaped chairs, even squashed and misshapen sofas – at least in the short-term.

However if you spend a lot of time working at a desk or in front of a computer you will want to ensure that your chair is fit for your purpose. That does not mean you need to rush out and buy an expensive 'ergonomic' chair that will promise a lot but won't deliver very much. All that's required is a regular and not over-padded office chair which has a reasonably firm and level seat that is neither too high nor too low, which gives you a sense of your sitting bones, has a long back which you can rest against, positions your hip joints slightly higher than your knees, and allows you to place your feet on the ground. If you prefer a high-backed traditional chair you can experiment by placing a couple of thin paperback books under the back legs to get some elevation and tilt the seat forward. That will allow you to maintain freedom in your hip joints and sit in a more balanced way on downward-pointing sitting bones. If you use a chair with rollers it might be worth investing in a firm seat wedge, which is readily available at specialist high street 'back care' shops, as well as on the internet.

Probably the most damaging chair design is one which has a backward-sloping seat – stackable chairs and most car seats for instance. Over time sitting in that type of chair for long periods will tend to shorten and weaken a number of your muscles, including the hip flexors that connect the legs and back, thus setting up some of the conditions for chronic back pain. Your kinaesthetic sense is also likely to be adversely affected.

I'm not keen on kneeling chairs because of the downward pressure on the lower leg and the likelihood that circulation is restricted. I cannot emphasise too much that there is a huge biomechanical and kinaesthetic advantage in having an ordinary chair which allows you to put your feet on the floor and a back that you can rest against from time to time.

Do I always have to use a carpeted floor to carry out Alexander lying down?

No. The reason a carpeted floor is recommended is that it generates the right kind of feedback to the back musculature since it is neither too soft nor too hard. But the instruction should not be taken too literally. Recently I asked a new student, who suffers from upper back and shoulder pain, how she was getting on with Alexander lying down, which we had gone through in the first couple of lessons. She replied that she had not been able to carry it out because her house had wooden floors which she found too hard to lie on. I was surprised at her response, but since it had not occurred to her, I suggested putting a mat or a blanket on the floor. 'That's a good idea,' she said. 'I'll try that.' And she has, with excellent results.

In addition to carrying out sessions on the floor Alexander lying down can also be performed when you are in bed. So if when you wake up you are not on your back, roll over so that your head is supported by one or more pillows. Now draw your knees up so that the soles of your feet are flat on the bed and spend a few minutes giving your directions. Then roll over in one of the ways you have learnt in lessons, sit on the edge of the bed and come to standing.

You can also perform Alexander lying down for a few minutes before you go to sleep. When you have finished roll on to your side. It's also a good idea to use a pillow that supports your head in such a way that your neck remains in line with the rest of the spine.

There's nothing to stop you improvising with Alexander lying down – it certainly shouldn't be thought of as an arcane ritual that can only be done at certain times and places. For example, if you are on holiday and sunbathing on the beach, or beside the pool, you can use a few paperback books or a folded towel placed on a pile of sand or pebbles as a head rest. And if you're lucky enough to be flying in business or first class on a long haul flight then put the seat into the horizontal mode and carry out some Alexander lying down.

One of my students, a dentist, tells me that at lunchtime he always lies on a carpeted floor in the surgery with his head supported by a small pile of magazines which he borrows from the waiting room. He finds that the practise dissipates the aches and pain caused by the morning surgery and leaves him fresh for the afternoon session. Another student who works as a journalist in a large open-plan newsroom, performs Alexander lying down underneath his desk every day after lunch. Not only is he able to give his directions but he reckons that he gets some of his best ideas for articles.

It would be nice to think that in the near future many more enlightened employers will allow workers to perform Alexander lying down at intervals during the working day in order to get into better shape and liberate their creativity.

Some elderly people have trouble getting on and off the floor. If this is the case with you, then perform your Alexander lying down on a reasonably firm bed or a flat sofa.

Apart from Alexander lying down, how else can I work on myself between lessons?

To a large extent it depends where you are in the process of learning the Alexander Technique. If you are a beginner you might wish to give attention to aspects of your everyday routine at different points in the day. For example, when you are getting ready for bed try to move a bit more slowly than normal and practise inhibiting and giving your directions as you take your clothes off and put another set on. When you wake up take your time getting out of bed and give the directions for the primary control as you brush your teeth, shower, get dressed and have breakfast. Around lunchtime it is always a good idea to take a break. You might want to take the opportunity to go for a walk whilst giving your directions. You can also start to think about other activities, such as getting in and out of the chair as you have been taught in lessons. And you will want to give some attention to how you sit, especially if your work involves sitting in front of a computer, or you have to attend frequent meetings

Later when you have been taught monkey, squatting, lunging, hands over the back of a chair, going on to the toes, using the wall and so on, you can incorporate these activities into your everyday routine – but by thinking them through rather than performing them as conventional exercises. You do not have to be at home to carry them out – there will be plenty of opportunities to find a quiet place to perform one or more of these Alexander activities. These can be revitalising especially if you're feeling fatigued because you have been sitting for too long, or if you have experienced some sort of emotional upset.

Bear in mind also that the various Alexander positions or movements of mechanical advantage are not just 'ideal types' to be performed without an end in mind. We can incorporate them into everyday life. For example, monkey, which is all about lowering height by bending your knees while maintaining internal length and width, is relevant to a whole range of activities from using a broom, washing up or brushing your teeth to playing golf, riding a bike or snowboarding. Going on to the toes is relevant to picking a can of baked beans from the cupboard in the kitchen or top shelf in your local store. Hands over the back of a chair provides information about how you use arms and hands when you take your mobile phone

Above Monkey applied to BMX

from your pocket, or play the piano or violin. While thinking of going up and back from your ankles, when you are standing in a long queue, or on an overcrowded bus or train will give you something constructive to think about and will stop you from getting irritated or frustrated. The examples can be multiplied innumerable times for innumerable situations.

I suppose the main thing we all need to learn is that it's in our interests to pay conscious attention to how we are doing at least *some* of our everyday activities, rather than just doing everything according to habit. But remember you can adapt the core principle of the Alexander Technique – inhibition and direction as it applies to human reaction – to more or less anything.

You can also learn to cultivate your observational skills and see how others use themselves in everyday life with the aim of getting information that will help you improve your own coordination. Watch people you know – family, friends and work colleagues – as well as those you do not know in places such as streets, parks, and restaurants and on public transport and try to work out how they sit, stand, bend, walk, run, speak and gesticulate. That kind of observation will help you understand that you can analyse the movement patterns of others, as well as your own, without using words. It will also help you become aware of how society and its technologies, for better or worse, shape our bodies.

I have trouble maintaining the directions because, despite my best efforts, I keep trying to feel whether I am getting things right or not. Can you give me some advice?

If it's any consolation your experience is not unusual. Alexander had exactly the same problem, and in my experience everyone else who tries to learn the Alexander Technique finds this aspect of setting aside a habitual kinaesthetic sense challenging. It will be worth your while reading the chapters 'Evolution of a Technique' and 'Use and Functioning in Relation to Reaction' in *The Use of the Self*, which Alexander wrote as a blueprint for the trainees on the first teacher training course. You'll see that a key lesson Alexander wants to convey to the reader is the importance of trusting the directions rather than trying to feel 'right' by relying on what he calls 'automatic sensory guidance'.

Above Monkey applied to snowboarding

And it's worth remembering that Alexander used mirrors so that he could get immediate feedback about how he was using or misusing himself. There is no reason why you cannot do the same. Be aware that although digital technologies available on smartphones and the like are very useful in providing information about how you're using yourself they're not equivalent to that supplied by a full-length mirror, which gives you real-time as well as full-size information.

From a practical point of view, whether you're using the mirrors or not, it's very important to keep looking out, seeing something and maintaining awareness of your immediate environment, in performing any directed activity, otherwise the temptation to go inside and feel it out to find out whether you are on the right track or not will be overwhelming. Visualisation – for example, thinking that you have a piece of string attached to the crown of your head to encourage your head to release forward and up – is not of much use since it too is based on a habitual feeling sense. Another disadvantage is that it takes your attention away from the present. In the final analysis it's almost as if you have to give up caring whether you are right or not. Just take the plunge by giving the directions, try to maintain them as you perform the movement and hope for the best!

If despite your best efforts a movement or activity doesn't work it doesn't matter because you can always have another go. In any case you will have learned something. If you keep trying to rely on feeling 'right' for guidance, you won't get very far, because your sensory habits will not let you.

Could you explain a bit more about the reasons for looking out to see something?

Alexander often remarked that there is an important relationship between the working of the eyes and the primary control. It was for that reason that he discouraged his students from blanking off. He would say, 'You're not looking out; you're not seeing something!' To get the message across he would on occasion ask a student to look at a painting on the wall of his teaching room, turn him or her around and ask for a description. In that way the student was activating both the visual sense and the memory, which as you know is also an important part of learning the Alexander Technique.

Although Alexander neither believed in nor recommended specific eye exercises he would often suggest to students to take their glasses off when having a lesson so that the eyes could work in a different way. And he was always alert to the fact that ill-fitting glasses, especially bifocals, might cause a student to stiffen the neck and pull the head back.

We also need to take into account that nowadays many of us sit in buildings for hours on end staring at screens of one sort or another. The truth is that we're not very well adapted for this type of close work, especially if it is performed in artificial light. Our eyes work better if they're used to interpret complex visual fields in natural light. It underlines the reason why when working in the office or at home you should take frequent breaks.

But once working freely your eyes exert a significant influence on your neck muscles, based upon the transmission of visual information from the retina to the brain via the optic nerve, a hugely important part of the central nervous system. The correct relationship can be observed in a toddler taking her first steps. With a lengthening direction along the spine and a freely poised head she will be drawn forwards by something bright and shiny that catches her attention on the other side of the room. Put only slightly metaphorically, the eyes lead, and everything else follows.

In many adults with stiffened necks more efficient working of the eyes generates a subtle release in the small and deep suboccipital neck muscles, which then radiates outwards to the larger neck muscles such as the scalenes, trapezius and sternocleidomastoids. With the eyes working independently, in combination with directions for a better working of the primary control, your head will pivot more easily on the topmost vertebra of the spine facilitating a release in the body's musculature. Do keep in mind that you're not doing anything directly to re-position the head. Allowing your eyes to look out so as to indirectly correct the problem of the head pulled down on the neck is a much better way of obtaining release than, say, actively dipping or dropping your nose or chin, which run a considerable risk of collapsing your neck forward and down, and depressing the larynx.

You will observe that although many world-class 100 m sprinters run in lanes in a sort of trance looking straight ahead towards the finish line, by contrast well-coordinated middle and long-distance runners, such as the legendary British runner Steve Ovett, as well as more recent

Above Ethiopia's triple Olympic champion Kenenisa Bekele using his eyes to good effect whilst maintaining perfect head balance

examples, including Ethiopia's Kenenisa Bekele, Haile Gebrselaisse and Tirunesh Dibaba, use their eyes a lot while racing as they need to take into account what their competitors are up to. That pattern of remaining alert can be observed not just when athletes are running in a pack and need to be careful of clipping the heels of other runners as they jostle for position, but also when they are leading the field and are looking up and down the track. That oscillation of the eyes provides information about the general direction of travel as well as the place where the feet are about to land. Whether they know it or not, well-coordinated athletes are activating the eyes-neck-head balance mechanism in movement I've just outlined.

You should also know that the eyes can be tremendously helpful in generating efficient movement. The rule is that if you wish to look side to side or up and down, inhibit and then allow the eyes to lead before letting the head and, if appropriate, the rest of the body to follow.

You place a great emphasis on antagonistic actions. Why?

It's one of the most neglected concepts in the Alexander Technique, although it shouldn't be because it has great explanatory power. Antagonistic actions – what Alexander more colloquially called antagonistic pulls – captures conceptually something of the physical reality that is brought about when you give the mental directions so that two or more opposing parts of the body are releasing away from each other, generating a dynamic elastic stretch.

A good example is when you are in monkey or a deep squat. Even though you are in a flexed position you are asking for your neck to release so that your head goes forward and up, your hips to release back and down, your knees to go forward and away, your feet to open into the ground and your shoulders to release away from each other. You will appreciate that what's happening at a deep neuromuscular level is way beyond anything that can be achieved through static stretching because so many different parts of the body are releasing into elastic length in opposing directions. An added bonus is that over time you will develop a more accurate kinaesthetic sense.

It's worth noting that although Alexander was still working out the implications, in *Introduction to a New Method of Respiratory Vocal Re-Education*, a pamphlet published in 1906, he refers to antagonistic actions as the 'great principle' underlying his technique.

Can I apply the Alexander Technique to hatha yoga?

No reason why not. The Alexander Technique can be applied to a range of activities from dancing and swimming to golf and cricket. But it is important to understand that the distinction made by Alexander between 'means' and 'ends' – the process rather than the goal – really is important. Accordingly, if you want to perform an action then it's best to perform it with the best degree of coordination possible, thinking out how you do it rather than just doing it, or by

Above Two women performing Natarajasana, one (left) with with poise, the other (right) with tension

imitating someone, both of which will trigger habitual responses and sensory pathways.

A few of my students are keen on hatha yoga – they value the experience of being in a class with like-minded people as well as the fact that they are learning something new. However when they tell me about a new yoga pose or movement they have learnt, and I ask them to perform it while I monitor what's going on, it's invariably the case that they don't give much attention to how it's being performed from an Alexander Technique perspective. In short they tend to stiffen rather than release into movement.

In the absence of getting feedback from an Alexander teacher, is there a better way to perform yoga when you are left to your own devices? There has to be. I think the best piece of advice is to observe and analyse how a skilled yoga teacher as well as how your classmates perform an activity – remember you are looking for positives and negatives from everyone involved – as well as studying other yoga practitioners on DVDs and social media sites. Without directly imitating what you have seen take some time to consider and think out how and if it would be possible for you to move. This is particularly important when performing backward-bending (hyperextension) asanas as you do not want to damage the delicate, wedge-shaped vertebrae of your lower back. You could try out various movements while maintaining your directions, ideally using a mirror to get accurate feedback.

It may well be the case that you cannot achieve the same final result as the teacher or others in your class if you stick to maintaining a good working of the primary control, because your body will not let you without causing undue strain. One way of monitoring this, whether or not feedback from a mirror is available, is the effect on your breathing. If you find that you're holding your breath or you're struggling to breathe because you're fixing or distorting the rib cage, it's a clear signal of misuse. As Alexander rightly noted 'all "physical" tension tends to cause thoracic (chest) rigidity and breathlessness (lack of respiratory control)'.

You then have a choice. You can either carry on doing whatever it is that you are doing, or give your directions and then see if you can perform the activity in a different way with a more efficiently working primary control. If you choose the latter option you should be prepared to accept that you might be performing an asana in a very different way to your teacher and classmates.

What about going to the gym?

The same sort of argument I've just sketched for hatha yoga applies. The key question is: can I do what I'm doing in such a way that I'm not losing internal length and fixing my rib cage. You want to be very aware of not making unnecessary tension, especially in the muscle systems that do not have to be directly involved. Most gyms nowadays have full-length mirrors so you can see what you're up to. If you can carry out activities without disturbing the balance of the head upon the neck and shortening the stature, go ahead and do what you want.

But if you've not already done so do pay a visit to the free weights section of any gym. You will observe people with screwed up faces, heads pulled back hard, and locked rib cages, doing their utmost to lift those extra kilograms. In this situation the 'need' to lift those weights is overwhelming and it's all too evident that grunting and breathlessness has become a badge of honour. It's another very good example of 'end-gaining'. That said, it's possible to use all of the equipment in the gym in a free and open way, but that takes time and thought. So if after due consideration you decide that the gym is not for you, consider another form of exercise such as Alexander walking and running, or applying the technique to riding a bike or swimming.

Above A man using a dumbbell but contracting throughout his body

Is the primary control the same thing as core stability?

The term core stability, which refers to the corset of muscle and connective tissue that encircles the spine and gives it support, has become a global buzzword. However it means something entirely different from Alexander's rather less well known idea of the primary control that a certain use of the head and neck in relation to the rest of the body improves general coordination.

Core stability, as well as associated ideas such as core strength and core conditioning, rose to prominence after a theory was proposed by a team of researchers at the University of Queensland in the mid-1990s that the delayed firing of specific abdominal and back muscles – transverse abdominis and multifidus respectively – is a cause of chronic lower back pain. A treatment programme was then devised for patients using real-time ultrasound monitoring that activated these muscles under medical supervision. It's a procedure still in use today.

Much to the surprise of the original researchers, however, a technique of drawing the navel towards the spine, preceded by lifting the pelvic floor, in an attempt to activate transverse abdominis, a practice known as 'zip and hollowing' or 'hollowing in', was taken up by a wide variety of practitioners, including many Pilates instructors and personal trainers. Amongst the latter group, for example, it has become fashionable to get clients to sit on a Swiss ball, pull in the belly button and perform abdominal crunches, or to press the back against the floor, hollow the stomach and move one spinal segment at a time while doing sit-ups.

Thankfully this practice has not gone unchallenged. Physical therapist Carolyn Richardson, who led the University of Queensland study and coined the term 'core stability', says: 'I have found that for the fitness industry it is often a poor instruction that is often misinterpreted or carried out badly. It's easily done incorrectly by people holding their breath or rounding their backs because they are sucking in their muscles so far.' World-renowned spine biomechanics expert Stuart McGill goes further. 'The idea has reached trainers and through them the public that the core means only the abs,' he observes. 'There's no science behind that idea. If you

Above A group performing abdominal crunches

hollow in, you bring the muscles closer to the spine, and you reduce the stability of the spine.'

Research on spinal loading forces using both computer models and test subjects in the laboratory has also resulted in McGill questioning the now widely-held assumption that transverse abdominis or multifidus play a central role in stability and balance. Instead he emphasises the significance of the way in which all the muscles of the torso as well as those that connect with the limbs bind and work together. I agree. On the other hand I don't agree with McGill that just because a number of movements, such as hitting a golf ball, lifting a heavy, loaded bar above the head in weightlifting, or throwing a punch in karate or boxing, involve muscular contraction that it is a good idea for people whilst standing upright to create moments of 'super stiffness' by bracing the entire abdominal wall (as if you were about to be punched in the stomach) and tightening the back extensor musculature.

Why? Well it's clear that focusing on contracting a particular muscle or larger muscle group interferes with the balance and efficient working of the body as a whole. More specifically from an Alexander Technique perspective if you directly brace the abdominal musculature (including transverse abdominis, rectus abdominis, and the external and internal obliques) and shorten the back musculature in the pursuit of what McGill calls 'torso stability' you will lose internal length, use too much effort by over contracting fatiguable muscle fibres and adversely affect your general coordination and functioning, including your ability to breathe efficiently – something which obviously depends on the capacity of your rib cage to move freely.

Furthermore actively bracing the abdominals and contracting the back extensor muscles will also narrow your field of attention because you're now trying to feel it out rather than looking out and taking in your environment. For a variety of reasons, then, I think it's much better to develop appropriate strength by activating a better working of your eyes and your head, neck and back relationship, and then putting a muscular demand on the system – whether that's through hitting a golf ball, performing a clean and jerk, throwing a punch or something else. There really is no need to micromanage the process.

If you want to develop better muscle tone then use any of the more dynamic Alexander positions of mechanical advantage, such as monkey, squatting, rotating backward and forward from the hip joints in a chair, lunging, going on to the toes, or using the wall with an efficient working of your primary control and limbs. Of course if you are able you can also perform hands over the back of a chair. All these activities will help to prevent muscle atrophy, caused by the loss of red muscle fibres or through habitual muscle shortening (or both) in a way that's impossible to achieve through conventional exercise regimes.

Also never underestimate the usefulness of a thoughtful but purposeful walk in creating and maintaining muscular strength and flexibility. Start slowly and then when well-coordinated increase your speed of travel. While walking you will want to maintain a thought of releasing up through the middle of your torso into the head around eye level and allow yourself to spin freely around the spinal axis.

To sum up: the Alexander Technique does not teach 'core stability' but is concerned with whole body stability, strength and conditioning through learning better balance and an improved kinaesthetic sense. Alas, unless you are putting this into practice while working as a full-time athlete or dancer, you probably won't end up with six-pack abs. Nevertheless you'll certainly have learned a skill-set that has major implications for your long-term health and well-being.

A final thought. Although natural selection never generates a perfect match between a species and the environment(s) in which it currently exists – our bodies have, after all, been shaped by the selective pressures of the past – we know for sure that we are adapted to be physically highly active. So in assessing the efficacy of exercise and exercise systems of one sort or another, it is useful to reflect on the fact that some contemporary peoples, such as the nomadic Hadza, provide a good (though probably not the only) model of human activity that fits very well with our biological inheritance and evolutionary history. Moreover when Hadza men, women and children go about their busy, daily routines, they carry out a wide range of movements, including standing, walking, jogging, running, jumping, squatting, sitting on the ground, kneeling, going on to the toes, lunging, climbing, using implements of one sort or another, carrying loads, speaking, singing, dancing and lying down.

Of course modern lifestyles are very different from those of hunter-gatherers, or even those of our grandparents. The invention and diffusion of innovative technologies which have, for the vast majority of us, led to the abolition of manual labour and the growth of employment in the sedentary service sector, is one of the great stories of our time. So too is the fact that many of us don't have to leave our homes to find food; we can buy more or less everything we need or desire via the internet, and those goods will be almost instantly delivered to our door. Consequently most of us in the developed world live comfortable, cosseted lives, which is sometimes an advantage and sometimes not, especially if we succumb to relative physical inactivity. This can cause, or at least contribute to, what the emerging field of evolutionary medicine categorises as lifestyle or 'mismatch' diseases – non-communicable conditions such as obesity, Type 2 diabetes, hypertension, stroke, flat feet, plantar fasciitis, some cancers and much lower back pain – that occur because our bodies are poorly or inadequately adapted to the new environments which we have constructed for ourselves.

We can though learn to become more active both at work and in our leisure time. But if we want to boost the chances of leading healthy, productive lives, increasing the amount of activity by itself is not enough. We need to pay attention to *how* we move. So we can use the Alexander Technique in all our activities, including standing, sitting, walking, running and other more complex movements. Put simply, we can think in everyday activity.

But please don't take my word for it, find out for yourself!

Bibliography

FM Alexander's books and works

Constructive Conscious Control of the Individual, Mouritz, 2004

Man's Supreme Inheritance, Mouritz, 2011

The Universal Constant in Living, Mouritz, 2000

The Use of the Self, Victor Gollancz, 1987

Articles and Lectures, edited by Jean M O Fischer, Mouritz, 2011

F M Alexander 1949-50 DVD, Mouritz, 2010

Books on Alexander and the Alexander Technique

Marjory Barlow and Séan Carey, Alexander Technique: the Ground Rules, HITE Publishing, 2011

Wilfred Barlow, The Alexander Principle, Gollancz, 1973

Wilfred Barlow, editor, More Talk of Alexander, Mouritz, 2005

Goddard Binkley, The Expanding Self, STAT Books, 1993

Michael Bloch, F M: The Life of Frederick Matthias Alexander, Little, Brown, 2004

Walter Carrington and Seán Carey, Explaining the Alexander Technique: The Writings of F Matthias Alexander, Mouritz, 2004

Walter Carrington and Seán Carey, Personally Speaking, Mouritz, 2001

David Garlick, editor, Proprioception, Posture and Emotion, The University of New South Wales, 1982

David Garlick, The Lost Sixth Sense: A Medical Scientist Looks at The Alexander Technique, The University of New South Wales, 1990

Frank Pierce Jones, Freedom to Change: The Development and Science of the Alexander Technique, Mouritz, 1996

Judy Leibowitz, Dare To Be Wrong, American Center for the Alexander Technique, 2007

Patrick Macdonald, The Alexander Technique As I See It, Rahula Books, 1989

Alexander D Murray, F M Alexander: In his own words and in the words of those who knew him, Blurb.com, 2011

John Nicholls and Séan Carey, The Alexander Technique, The Brighton Alexander Training Centre, 1991

Lulie Westfeldt, F Matthias Alexander: The Man and His Work, Mouritz, 1998

Social and Cultural Anthropology

Michael Carrithers, Why Humans Have Cultures: Explaining Anthropology and Social Diversity, Oxford University Press, 1992

Thomas J Csordas, editor, Embodiment and Experience: The Existential Ground of Culture and Self, Cambridge University Press, 1994

Mary Douglas, Natural Symbols: Explorations in Cosmology, Barrie and Rockliff/Cresset Press, 1970

Thomas Hylland Eriksen, Small Places, Large Issues, Pluto Press, 2010

Robert L Kelly, The Lifeways of Hunter-Gatherers: The Foraging Spectrum, Cambridge University Press, 2013

Frank Marlowe, The Hadza Hunter-Gatherers of Tanzania, University of California Press, 2010

Barbara D Miller, Cultural Anthropology, Pearson, 2012

Paul Spencer, The Samburu: A Study in Geocentracy, Routledge, 2004

James Woodburn, Hunters and Gatherers: The Material Culture of the Nomadic Hadza, Trustees of the British Museum, 1970

Biological Anthropology and Evolutionary Biology

Raymond Dart, *Skill and Poise*, STAT Books, 2006

Charles Darwin, *The Expression of the Emotions in Man and Animals*, Penguin Classics, 2009

Robin Dunbar, *The Human Story*, Faber and Faber, 2005

Robin Dunbar, *Human Evolution*, Pelican Books, 2014

Peter Gluckman and Mark Hanson, *Mismatch: The Lifestyle Diseases Timebomb*, Oxford University Press, 2006

Peter Gluckman et al, *Principles of Evolutionary Medicine*, Oxford University Press, 2009

Jonathan Kingdon, *Lowly Origin: Where, When and Why our Ancestors First Stood Up*, Princeton University Press, 2003

Daniel Lieberman, *The Evolution of the Human Head*, Harvard University Press, 2011

Daniel Lieberman, *The Story of the Human Body: Evolution, Health, and Disease*, Allen Lane, 2013

Svante Pääbo, *Neanderthal Man : In Search of Lost Genomes*, Basic Books, 2014

Robert W Shumaker et al, *Animal Tool Behavior: The Use and Manufacture of Tools by Animals*, The John Hopkins University Press, 2011

Craig Stanford, *Upright: The Evolutionary Key to Becoming Human*, Houghton Mifflin Company, 2003

Craig Stanford, *Planet Without Apes*, Harvard University Press, 2012

Philip V Tobias, *Man, the Tottering Biped: The Evolution of His Posture, Poise and Skill*, University of New South Wales, 1982

Marlene Zuk, *Paleofantasy: What Evolution Really Tells Us About Sex, Diet and How We Live*, W W Norton & Company, 2013

Other recommended books

Manuel Castells, *Communication Power*, Oxford University Press, 2009

Stanley Coren, *Sleep Thieves: An Eye-Opening Exploration into the Science and Mysteries of Sleep*, The Free Press, 1996

Galen Cranz, *The Chair: Rethinking Culture, Body and Design*, Norton, 2000

William C Dement, *The Promise of Sleep: A Pioneer in Sleep Medicine Explores the Vital Connection Between Health, Happiness, and a Good Night's Sleep*, Random House, 2000

Adharanand Finn, *Running with the Kenyans: Discovering the secrets of the fastest people on earth*, Faber and Faber, 2012

Erving Goffman, *The Presentation of Self in Everyday Life*, Penguin Books, 1990

Serge Gracovetsky, *The Spinal Engine*, Springer-Verlag, 1988

Stuart McGill, *Low Back Disorders*, Human Kinetics, 2007

Lucy Pratt and Linda Woolley, *Shoes*, V&A Publishing, 2008

Charles Scott Sherrington, *The Endeavour of Jean Fernel*, Cambridge University Press, 1946

Articles

Karen Adolph et al, How do you learn to walk? Thousands of steps and dozens of falls per day, *Psychological Science*, 23, 1387-1394, 2012

Robert McNeill Alexander, Bipedal animals, and their differences from humans, *Journal of Anatomy*, 204, 5, 321-330, 2004

Renato Bender et al, *The Savannah Hypotheses: Origin, Reception and Impact on Paleoanthropology, History and Philosophy of the Life Sciences, 34, 1-2, 147-184, 2012*

Chintan Bhatt et al, Variation in the insertion of the latissimus dorsi & its clinical importance, *Journal of Orthopaedics*, 10, 1, 25-28, 2013

Paul M Bingham, Human Uniqueness: A General Theory, *The Quarterly Review of Biology*, 74, 2, 133-169, 1999

Franco Bocci, Whether or not to run in the rain, *European Journal of Physics*, 33, 5, 1321 – 1322, 2012

Dennis Bramble and Daniel Lieberman, Endurance running and the evolution of Homo, *Nature*, 432, 345 – 352, 2004

William Brandler et al, Common variants in left/right asymmetry genes and pathways are associated with relative hand skill, PLoS *Genetics* 9, 9: e1003751. doi:10.1371/journal. pgen.1003751, 2013

Helen Branthwaite et al, Footwear choices made by young women and their potential impact on foot health, *Journal of Health Psychology*, 18, 11, 1422-1431, 2013

Tim Cacciatore et al, Prolonged weight-shift and altered spinal coordination during sit-to-stand in practitioners of the Alexander Technique, *Gait & Posture*, 34, 4, 496 – 501, 2011

Tim Cacciatore et al, Increased dynamic regulation of postural tone through Alexander Technique Training, *Human Movement Science*, 30, 1, 74 – 89, 2011

Robert Capasco et al, On muscle, tendons and high heels, *The Journal of Experimental Biology*, 213, 2582 – 2588, 2010

Seán Carey, The Multi-Ethnic Wall, *New Society*, 19 April, 99 – 100, 1984

Seán Carey, The secret of East African running success, *The Independent*, August 6, 2012

David Carrier, The energetic paradox of human running and hominid evolution, *Current Anthropology*, 25, 4, 483 – 495, 1984

Susana Carvalho et al, Tool-composite reuse in wild chimpanzees (Pan troglodytes): archaeologically invisible steps in the technological evolution of early hominins? *Animal Cognition*, 12, 1, 103 – 114, 2009

Susana Carvalho et al, Chimpanzee carrying behaviour and the origins of human bipedality, *Current Biology*, 22, 6, 180 – 181, 2012

Sheldon Cohen et al, Emotional style and susceptibility to the common cold, *Psychosomatic Medicine*, 65, 4, 652-657, 2003

Sheldon Cohen et al, Chronic stress, glucocorticoid receptor resistance, inflammation, and disease risk, *Proceedings of the National Academy of Sciences*, 109,16, 5995-5999, 2012

Steven H Collins et al, Dynamic arms swinging in human walking, *Proceedings of the Royal Society B: Biological Sciences*, 276, 3679 –3688, 2009

Meghan M Cotter et al, Human evolution and osteoporosis-related spinal fractures, *PLoS ONE*, 6, 10: e26658. doi:10.1371/journal. pone.0026658, 2011

Robin H Crompton et al, Locomotion and posture from the common hominoid ancestor to fully modern hominins, with special reference to the last common panin/hominin ancestor, *Journal of Anatomy*, 212, 4, 501-543, 2008

Alberto Cruz-Martin et al, A dedicated circuit links direction-selective retinal ganglion cells to the primary visual cortex, *Nature*, 507, 7492, 358-361, 2014

Christopher Cunningham et al, The influence of foot posture on the cost of transport in humans, *The Journal of Experimental Biology*, 213, 790 – 797, 2010

Justin R Davis et al, The relationship between fear of falling and human postural control, *Gait & Posture*, 29, 2, 275-279, 2009

Justin R Davis et al, Human proprioceptive adaptations during states of height-induced fear and anxiety, *Journal of Neurophysiology*, 106, 3082-3090, 2011

Jeremy M DeSilva, and Simone V Gill, Brief communication: A midtarsal (midfoot) break in the human foot, *American Journal of Physical Anthropology* 151, 3, 495-499, 2013

Katherine Dolan and Ann Green, Lumbar spine reposition sense: the effect of a 'slouched posture', *Manual Therapy*, 11, 3, 202 – 207, 2006

S Boyd Eaton et al, Evolutionary health promotion: a consideration of common counterarguments, *Preventive Medicine*, 34, 2, 119 – 123, 2002

Charlotte Edwardson et al, Association of sedentary behaviour with metabolic syndrome, *PLoS ONE*, 7, 4, e34916. doi:10.1371/journal. pone.0034916, 2012

Kirk Erickson et al, Exercise as a Way of Capitalizing on Neuroplasticity in Late Adulthood, *Topics in Geriatric Rehabilitation*, 30, 1, 8-14, 2014

Ron Erlich et al, The effect of jaw clenching on the electromyographic activities of 2 neck and 2 trunk muscles, *Journal of Orofacial Pain*, 13,2, 115-120, 1999

Daniel P Ferris et al, Moving the arms to move the legs, *Exercise and Sports Science Reviews*, 34, 3, 113 – 116, 2006

Philip Gable and Eddie Harmon-Jones, Approach-motivated positive affect reduces breadth of attention, *Psychological Science*, 19, 5, 476 - 482, 2008

Julianna Gal, Mammalian spinal biomechanics: postural support in seated macaques, *The Journal of Experimental Biology*, 205, 1703–1707, 2002

Michael E Gerling and Stephen H M Brown, Architectural analysis and predicted functional capability of the human latissimus dorsi muscle, *Journal of Anatomy*, 223, 2, 112-122, 2013

Sander L Gilman 'Stand Up Straight': Notes Toward a History of Posture, *Journal of Medical Humanities*, 35, 1, 57-83, 2013

Erving Goffman, Embarrassment and social organization, *American Journal of Sociology*, 62, 3, 264-271, 1956

Irene Di Gulio et al, The proprioceptive and agonist roles of gastrocnemius, soleus and tibialis anterior muscles in maintaining human upright posture, *The Journal of Physiology*, 587, 10, 2399-2416, 2009

Irene Di Gulio et al, Human standing: does the control strategy preprogram a rigid knee? *Journal of Applied Physiology*, 114, 12, 1717-1729, 2013

Eddie Harmon-Jones and Carly Peterson, Supine body position reduces neural response to anger evocation, *Psychological Science*, 20, 1209–1210, 2009

Lee Herrington and Ian Horsley, Effects of latissimus dorsi length on shoulder flexion in canoeists, swimmers, rugby players, and controls, *Journal of Sport and Health Science*, 3,1, 60-63, 2014

Yoichiro Hirasawa et al, Postural changes of the dural sac in the lumbar spines of asymptomatic individuals using positional stand-up magnetic resonance imaging, *Spine*, 32, 4, 136-140, 2007

William D Hopkins et al, The neural and cognitive correlates of aimed throwing in chimpanzees: a magnetic resonance image and behavioural study on a unique form of social tool use, *Philosophical Transactions of the Royal Society B: Biological Sciences*, 367, 1585, 37-47, 2012.

Signe Howell, 'To be angry is not to be human but to be fearful is' in *Societies at Peace: Anthropological Perspectives*, edited by Signe Howell and Roy Willis, 45-59, Routledge, 1989

Sarah B Hrdy, Development + Social Selection in the Emergence of 'Emotionally Modern' Humans, *New Frontiers in Social Neuroscience*, 21, 57-91, 2014

David Hryvniak, Barefoot running survey: Evidence from the field, *Journal of Sport and Health Science*, 3, 2, 131-136, 2014

Tim Jones and Lesley Glover, Exploring the psychological processes underlying touch: lessons from the Alexander Technique, *Clinical Psychology & Psychotherapy*, 21, 2, 140-153, 2014

Françoise K Jouffroy and Monique F Médina, A Hallmark of Humankind: The Gluteus Maximus Muscle in *Human Origins and Environmental Backgrounds*, edited by Hidemi Ishida et al, 135-148, Springer, 2006

Lana B Karasik et al, WEIRD walking: Cross-cultural research on motor development, *Behavioural Brain Sciences*, 33, 2-3, 95-96, 2010

Lana B Karasik et al, Transition from crawling to walking and infants' actions with objects and people, *Child Development*, 82, 4, 1199-1209, 2011

Peter Larson, Comparison of foot strike patterns of barefoot and minimally shod runners in a recreational road race, *Journal of Sport and Health Science*, 3, 2, 137-142, 2014

Jean-Baptiste Leca et al, Stone-throwing by Japanese macaques: form and functional aspects of a group-specific behavioural tradition, *Journal of Human Evolution*, 55, 989 – 998, 2008

Louis Liebenberg, Persistence hunting by modern hunter-gatherers, *Current Anthropology*, 47, 6, 1017 – 1026, 2006

Louis Liebenberg, The relevance of persistence hunting to human evolution, *Journal of Human Evolution*, 55, 1156-1159, 2008

Daniel Lieberman, What We Can Learn About Running from Barefoot Running: An Evolutionary Medical Perspective, *Exercise Science Sports Review*, 40, 63-72, 2012

Daniel Lieberman, Strike type variation among Tarahumara Indians in minimal sandals versus conventional running shoes, *Journal of Sport and Health Science*, 3, 2, 86-94, 2014

Paul Little et al, Randomised control trial of Alexander technique lessons, exercise and massage (ATEAM) for chronic and recurrent back pain, *BMJ: British Medical Journal*, 2008

Everett B Lohmann III et al, A comparison of the spatiotemporal parameters, kinematics, and biomechanics between shod, unshod, and minimally supported running as compared to walking, *Physical Therapy in Sport*, 12, 4, 151-163, 2011

Ian D Loram and Martin Lakie, Direct measurement of human ankle stiffness during quiet standing: the intrinsic mechanical stiffness is insufficient for stability, *The Journal of Physiology* 545, 3, 1041-1053, 2002.

Ian D Loram et al, The Consequences of Short-Range Stiffness and Fluctuating Muscle Activity for Proprioception of Postural Joint Rotations: The Relevance to Human Standing, *Journal of Neurophysiology*, 102, 1, 460-474, 2009

Ian D Loram et al, Paradoxical muscle movement during postural control, *Medicine + Science in Sports + Exercise*, 41, 1, 198-205, 2009

Tetsuro Matsuzawa, Comparative cognitive development, *Development Science*, 10, 1, 97 – 103, 2007

Stuart McGill, Core Training: Evidence Translating to Better Performance and Injury Prevention, *Strength & Conditioning Journal*, 32, 3, 33-46, 2010

Yuu Mizuno et al, Behavior of infant chimpanzees during the night in the first 4 months of life: smiling and suckling in relation to behavioral state, *Infancy*, 9, 2, 215 – 234, 2006

Steven Moore et al, Leisure time physical activity of moderate to vigorous intensity and mortality, *PLoS Med* 9, 11, e1001335. doi:10.1371/journal.pmed.1001335, 2012

Michael H Morgan and David R Carrier, Protective buttressing of the human fist and the evolution of hominin hands, *The Journal of Experimental Biology*, 216, 2, 236-244, 2013

Jared A Neilsen et al, An evaluation of the left-brain vs right-brain hypothesis with resting state functional connectivity magnetic resonance imaging, *PLoS ONE* 8, 8: e71275. doi:10.1371/journal.pone.0071275, 2013

Michael Nevitt et al, Very low prevalence of hip osteoarthritis among Chinese elderly in Beijing, China, compared with whites in the United States, *Arthritis and Rheumatism*, 46, 7, 1773-1779, 2002

Callum J Osler et al, Postural threat differentially affects the feedforward and feedback components of the vestibular-evoked balance response, *European Journal of Neuroscience*, 38, 8, 3239-3247, 2013

Janni Pedersen et al, Why apes point: Pointing gestures in spontaneous conversation of language-competent Pan/Homo Bonobos in *Primatology: Theories, Methods and Research*, edited by Emil Potocki and Juliusz Krasiñski, 53-74, Nova Publishers, 2009

Charles Perrault and Sarah Matthew, Dating the origin of language using phonemic diversity, *PloS ONE*, 7, 4, e35289, 2012

Herman Pontzer et al, Control and function of arm swing in human walking and running, *The Journal of Experimental Biology*, 212, 4, 523-534, 2009

Herman Pontzer et al, Hunter-gatherer energetics and human obesity, *PLoS ONE* 7(7): e40503. doi:10.1371/journal.pone.0040503, 2012

Herman Pontzer et al, Foot strike patterns and hind limb joint angles during running in Hadza hunter-gatherers, *Journal of Health and Sport Science*, 3, 95-101, 2014

Robert Provine, Walkie-talkie evolution: Bipedalism and vocal production, *Behavioral and Brain Sciences*, 27, 520 – 521, 2004

David A Raichlen et al, Wired to run: exercise-induced endocannabinoid signaling in humans and cursorial mammals with implications for the 'runner's high', *The Journal of Experimental Biology*, 15, 215, 1331–1336, 2012

David A Raichlen et al, Evidence of Lévy walk foraging patterns in human hunter–gatherers, *Proceedings of the National Academy of Sciences*, 111, 2, 728-733, 2014

Elodie Reghem et al, The influence of body posture on the kinematics of prehension in humans and gorillas (Gorilla gorilla), *Experimental Brain Research*, 232, 1-10, 2014

Neil T Roach et al, Elastic energy storage in the shoulder and the evolution of high-speed throwing in Homo, *Nature*, 498, 483-486, 2013

Karen Rosenberg and Wenda Trevathan, Birth, obstetrics and human evolution, *BJOG: An International Journal of Obstetrics & Gynaecology* 109, 1, 1199-1206, 2002.

Crickette Sanz et al, Design complexity in termite-fishing tools of chimpanzees (Pan troglodytes), *Biology Letters*, 5, 3, 293-296, 2009

Alwyn Scally and Richard Durbin, Revising the human mutation rate: Implications for understanding human evolution, *Nature Reviews Genetics*, 13, 10, 745-753, 2012

Nancy Scheper-Hughes and Margaret Lock, The mindful body, *Medical Anthropology Quarterly*, 1, 1, 6-41, 1987

Ian Spreadbury and Andrew Samis, Evolutionary Aspects of Obesity, Insulin Resistance, and Cardiovascular Risk, *Current Cardiovascular Risk Reports*, 7, 2, 136 – 146, 2013

Hideko Takeshita et al, The supine position of postnatal human infants: Implications for the development of cognitive intelligence, *Interaction Studies*, 10, 2, 252 – 268, 2010

Margaretha C Tersteeg et al, Cautious gait in relation to knowledge and vision of height: is altered visual information the dominant influence? *Journal of Neurophysiology*, 107, 2686-2691, 2012

Michael Tomasello et al, A New Look at Infant Pointing, *Child Development*, 78, 3, 705-722, 2007

Erik Trinkaus and Hong Shang, Anatomical evidence for the antiquity of human footwear: Tianyuan and Sunghir, *Journal of Archaeological Science*, 35, 1928 – 1933, 2008

James R Usherwood et al, The human foot and heel–sole–toe walking strategy: a mechanism enabling an inverted pendular gait with low isometric muscle force? *Journal of the Royal Society Interface*, 9, 75, 2396-2402, 2012

Hidde Van der Ploeg et al, Sitting time and all-cause mortality risk in 222497 Australian adults, *Archives of Internal Medicine*, 172, 6, 494-500, 2012

Taian M Vieira et al, Recruitment of motor units in the medial gastrocnemius muscle during human quiet standing: is recruitment intermittent? What triggers recruitment? *Journal of Neurophysiology*, 107, 2, 666-676, 2012

Justin N Wood et al, The uniquely human capacity to throw evolved from a non-throwing primate: an evolutionary dissociation between action and perception, *Biology letters*, 3, 4, 360-365, 2007

Justin N Wood and Marc D Hauser, Action comprehension in non-human primates: motor simulation or inferential reasoning, *Trends in cognitive sciences*, 12, 12, 461-465, 2008

Emma Wilmot et al, Sedentary time in adults and the association with diabetes, cardiovascular disease and death: Systematic review and meta-analysis, *Diabetologia*, 55, 2895-2905, 2012

John D Willson et al, Short-Term Changes in Running Mechanics and Foot Strike Pattern After Introduction to Minimalistic Footwear, *PM&R*, 6,1, 34-43, 2014

Isabelle Winder et al, Complex topography and evolution: the missing link, *Antiquity*, 87, 333 – 349, 2013

Lucy Yardley et al, Patients' views of receiving lessons in the Alexander Technique and an exercise prescription for managing back pain in the ATEAM trial, *Family Practice*, 27,2, 198-204 , 2010

Richard W Young, Evolution of the hand: the role of throwing and clubbing, *Journal of Anatomy*, 202, 1, 165-174, 2003

Yi Zhang et al, Association of squatting with increased prevalence of tibiofemoral knee arthritis, *Arthritis and Rheumatism*, 50, 4, 1187-1192, 2004

Useful contact

If you are interested in having lessons in the Alexander Technique in the UK or other parts of the world you can find information about the location of teachers by contacting the Society of Teachers of the Alexander Technique (STAT). Its website is a particularly good resource.

www.stat.org.uk

Picture Credits

Cover, Loretta Manson, *Ryan Carey*

Back Cover, Seán Carey and Loretta Manson, *N Thapen*

15, A female dancer performing turnout, *Shutterstock.com*

16, A young man communicating hyper-masculinity, *Shutterstock.com*

17, Two women sweep a section of Goa's Patnem Beach, *Holly Blake*

20, Alexander showing a student how to put hands over the back of a chair, *Courtesy of John Nicholls*

21, A Hadza man starting a fire, *Luisa Puccini/ Shutterstock.com*

22, A group of people gathered around and drawn into a screen, *Shutterstock.com*

23, Technological advances make possible new digital worlds, *Shutterstock.com*

26, F M Alexander (1869-1955) as a young actor, *photograph of F M Alexander by kind permission of The Walter Carrington Educational Trust. Copyright 2014. www.wcet.org.uk*

29, Lauren Bacall (1924-2014) and 'The Look', *alisonkerr.wordpress.com*

33, Henry Cotton (1907-1987), one of Alexander's students, *onbekend/commons.wikimedia.org*

35, Nikolaas Tinbergen (1907-1988), *Max Planck Gesellschaft/commons.wikimedia.org*

37, Alexander working with a student, *photograph of F M Alexander teaching Arthur Busch, c 1941, by kind permission of The Walter Carrington Educational Trust. Copyright 2014. www.wcet.org.uk*

41, Many of us subconsciously pull the head back and down, *Sally Barton*

43, Interplay between members of two primate species, *Shutterstock.com*

44, A Maasai woman and her children sitting in a very balanced way, *Shutterstock.com*

45, The ideological-emotional motif of upper class British men and women, *Shutterstock.com*

46, A group of young Samburu warriors, *Lorimer Images/Shutterstock.com*

47, Emotions play an important role in social bonding, *Shutterstock.com*

47, Rage against the machine, *Shutterstock.com*

49, Professor Sir Charles Sherrington (1857-1952), *Bain News Service/ commons.wikimedia.org*

50, Spine, *Shutterstock.com*

51, The trapezius is one of a set of muscles that attaches to the head, *Shutterstock.com*

52, Illustration of the atlanto-occipital joint, *Shutterstock.com*

53, A man riding a camel on Jumeirah Beach in Dubai, *Shutterstock.com*

54, The bones of the pelvis allow us to sit efficiently, *Shutterstock.com*

55, The hip joint, *Shutterstock.com*

58, Arsenal and England forward Theo Walcott, *Ronnie Macdonald/commons.wikimedia.org*

62, Carrying loads on the head is customary in many non-Western cultures, *gnomeandi/Shutterstock.com*

64, There are worse and better ways of picking objects off the floor, *Sally Barton*

66, A typical office meeting, *Shutterstock.com*

70, The centre of gravity in a quadruped chimpanzee, *Sally Barton*

72, On the left a typical upright slouch, *Sally Barton*

73, Balancing a book on the head, *Shutterstock.com*

75, Ivory Coast forward Didier Drogba, *mountainpix/ Shutterstock.com*

77, Jessica Ennis-Hill poised on tip-toe, *Ian Walton/ Getty Images Sport*

80, Going on to the toes on your own, *Sally Barton*

81, Using a wall to achieve better balance and coordination, *Sally Barton*

83, Walking away from the wall maintaining balance, *Sally Barton*

83, A girl reaching for an apple, *Shutterstock.com*

84, A Taekwondo martial artist performing an aerial kick, *Shutterstock.com*

88, John McEnroe about to serve, *Antonio García/ commons.wikimedia.org*

89, A baby gorilla demonstrates bipedal walking, *Shutterstock.com*

92, Allowing the eyes to initiate movement using the spiral mechanism, *Sally Barton*

93, Keeping your head freely poised allows a spiral movement in the body, *Ryan Carey*

94, A group of Hadza women, *Idobi/commons. wikimedia.org*

97, A group of friends walking, *Shutterstock.com*

98, Although we can walk in many different ways, *Sally Barton*

101, Carrying a bag or other items, *Shutterstock.com*

102, Two Hadza hunters walking back to camp with the day's catch, *Andreas Lederer/commons.wikimedia.org*

104, Children should maximise the time spent barefoot, *Shutterstock.com*

105, Christian Louboutin's high heels, *thepresidentwearsprada/commons.wikimedia.org*

108, A contemporary-style chair, *Shutterstock.com*

109, Three Hadza young men sitting on rocks, *erichon/ Shutterstock.com*

110, Sitting poorly places a great strain on the spine, *Shutterstock.com*

111, There are many different ways to sit on a chair, *Ryan Carey*

112, A simple way to find out how much you pull your head back, *Sally Barton*

118, Active sitting is relevant to a wide variety of situations, *Shutterstock.com*

119, Using the back of a chair for support, *Sally Barton*

120, Using the back of a sofa for support with ankles crossed, *Ryan Carey*

124, Modern time-poor, reluctant-to-bend consumers, *Shutterstock.com*

125, Vietnamese woman squatting well, *Staffan Scherz*

126, Not using the ankles, knees and hips properly compresses the spine, *Shutterstock.com*

127, A youngster squatting well, *Shutterstock.com*

128, Monkey in two stages, *Sally Barton*

131, Using a wall to perform monkey, *Sally Barton*

132, The use of positions of mechanical advantage by workers in rice fields in India, *Im Perfect Lazybones/ Shutterstock.com*

133, Swiss tennis champion Martina Hingis, *Robyn Wilson/Shutterstock.com*

134, Placing the hands on a firm surface, *N Thapen*

136, A blind Afghan man squatting, *Andy Barnham/ commons.wikimedia.org*

137, A man demonstrating the art of climbing a coconut tree in Kerala, India, *Shutterstock.com*

138, You can use a squat to lower your height, *Sally Barton*

139, It's all too easy to pull in the back, *Shutterstock.com*

142, Illustration of shoulder girdle, *Shutterstock.com*

143, A toddler pointing with his index finger, *Shutterstock.com*

144, A cricketer ready to bowl, *EcoPrint/ Shutterstock.com*

146, Lang Lang, *Andreas Praefcke/commons. wikimedia.org*

146, Artur Rubenstein, *Rossem, Wim van/Anefo/ commons.wikimedia.org*

147, Riverdance, *Jack.Q/Shutterstock.com*

148, Hip-hop has become a global phenomenon, *Eugenio Marongiu/Shutterstock.com*

149, Los Angeles-born urban dancer Jeffrey Daniel, *jeffreydaniel.com*

152, Performing hands over the back of a chair, *Ryan Carey*

153, Placing hands over the back of a chair, *Ryan Carey*

154, The latissimus dorsi muscles, *Shutterstock.com*

157, A woman preparing food, *Shutterstock.com*

158, Using a smartphone, *Shutterstock.com*

159, A man brushing his teeth with a power grip, *Shutterstock.com*

161, Thumbs up, *Shutterstock.com*

164, A baby lying on her back playing with her feet, *Shutterstock.com*

Index